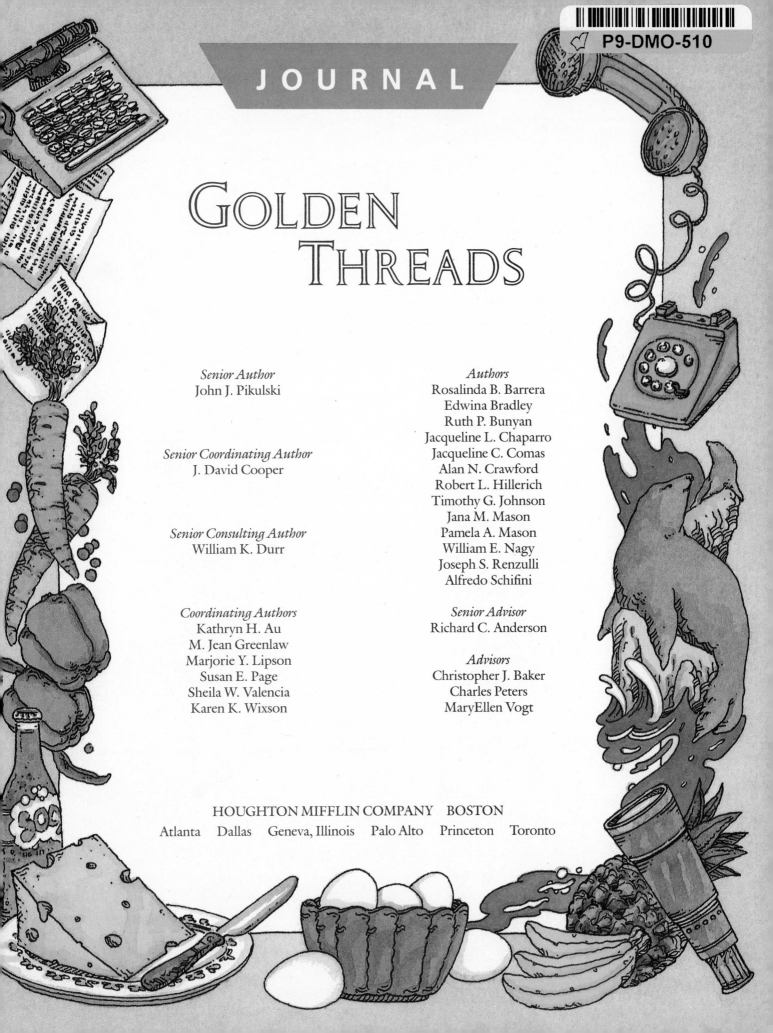

JOURNAL

Golden Threads

Senior Author
John J. Pikulski

Senior Coordinating Author
J. David Cooper

Senior Consulting Author
William K. Durr

Coordinating Authors
Kathryn H. Au
M. Jean Greenlaw
Marjorie Y. Lipson
Susan E. Page
Sheila W. Valencia
Karen K. Wixson

Authors
Rosalinda B. Barrera
Edwina Bradley
Ruth P. Bunyan
Jacqueline L. Chaparro
Jacqueline C. Comas
Alan N. Crawford
Robert L. Hillerich
Timothy G. Johnson
Jana M. Mason
Pamela A. Mason
William E. Nagy
Joseph S. Renzulli
Alfredo Schifini

Senior Advisor
Richard C. Anderson

Advisors
Christopher J. Baker
Charles Peters
MaryEllen Vogt

HOUGHTON MIFFLIN COMPANY   BOSTON
Atlanta   Dallas   Geneva, Illinois   Palo Alto   Princeton   Toronto

ISBN: 0-395-61970-X

1213-B-01009998

CONTENTS

CONTENTS

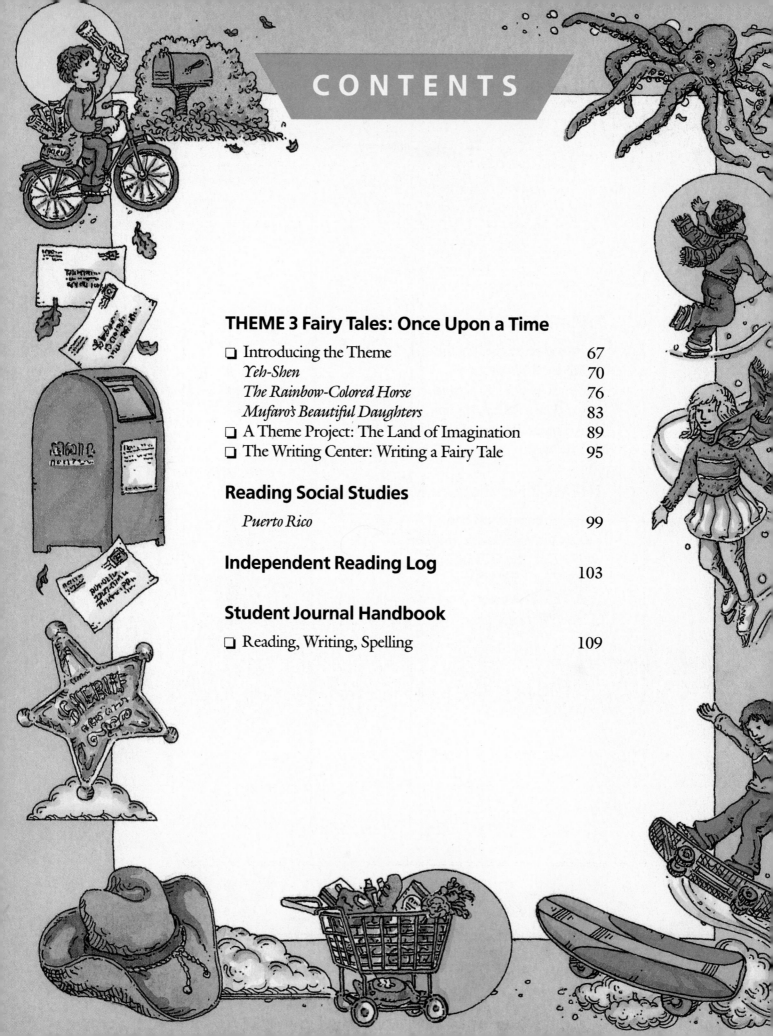

Beverly Cleary

Beverly Cleary Fan Club

Member's Name: _____

Date Club Activities Begin: _____

Date Club Activities End: _____

As a Member I Will

- Read three selections by Beverly Cleary
- Learn to understand characters and events in realistic stories
- Read and share other books by a favorite author
- Take a poll to find out people's favorite authors
- Write a realistic story and choose other writing projects to do

1

BOOKS I WANT TO READ

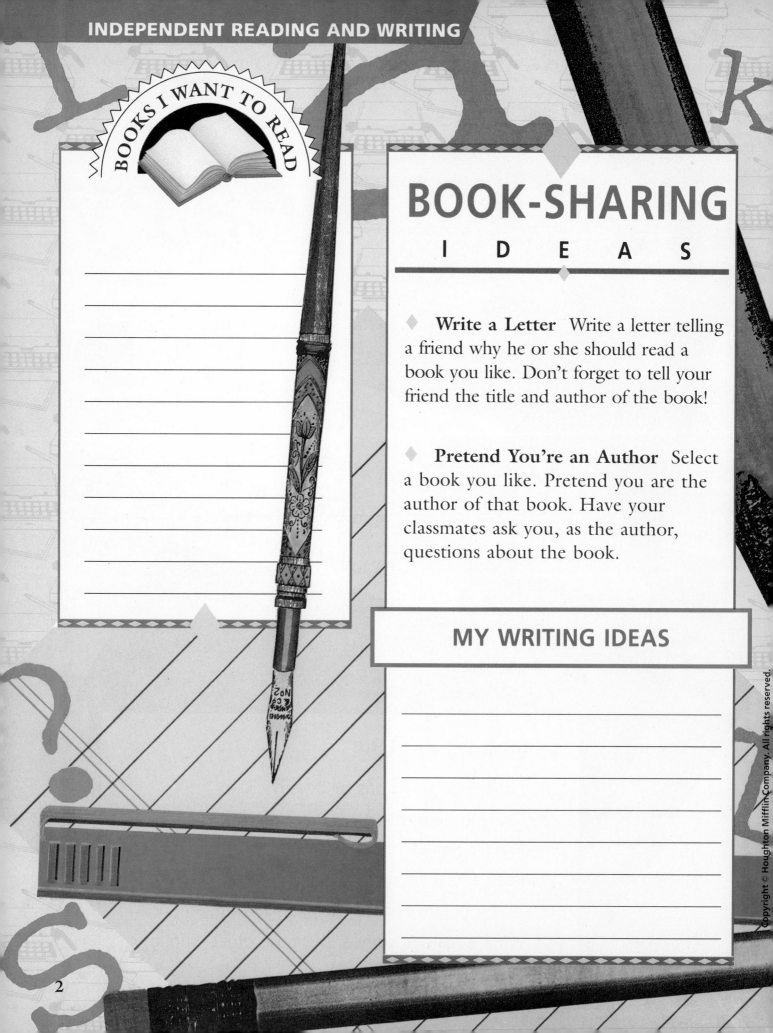

BOOK-SHARING
I D E A S

◆ **Write a Letter** Write a letter telling a friend why he or she should read a book you like. Don't forget to tell your friend the title and author of the book!

◆ **Pretend You're an Author** Select a book you like. Pretend you are the author of that book. Have your classmates ask you, as the author, questions about the book.

MY WRITING IDEAS

Beverly Cleary

Add to the chart below anything you know about the author Beverly Cleary and the kinds of stories she writes. After you finish reading the stories in this theme, come back to this page and add more information to the chart.

Kinds of Stories

Names of Characters

Beverly Cleary

Facts About the Author

Names of Stories

HENRY WRITES A LETTER

Older and Wiser  A younger brother or sister can sometimes be a problem! Draw two cartoons that show how a younger child can create problems for a big brother or sister. Write what each person is saying in the speech balloons.

Choose one of the problems you drew and tell how you could solve it. Think of a solution that would make both people happy.

_____

_____

_____

_____

_____

_____

Little Brother Was a Big Bother

Freddy wanted Lisa, his older sister, to pay **attention** to him. He did **annoying** things like making noise when she was trying to do her homework. He acted like a **pest**, refusing to leave his sister alone. At first Lisa tried to **ignore** him. She waited for him to stop his **mischief**. Then she turned around and said, "You are really being a **nuisance**."

"Who, me?" said Freddy with a grin.

Now answer these questions.

What is something that is **annoying** to you? _____

_____

_____

What is one thing that a **pest** or a **nuisance** might do? _____

_____

_____

What might you do to get someone's **attention**? _____

_____

_____

If you **ignore** someone, what are you doing?

_____

_____

What is one way someone could get into **mischief**? _____

_____

_____

5

Preview and Predict Preview the story. Then predict who you think Henry will write a letter to and why.

_____

_____

_____

Monitoring Comprehension

1. Read to the end of page 17. Draw a picture that shows Henry's problem. Then answer the questions.

What was Henry's problem?

_____

_____

Who did Henry ask for advice?

_____

_____

Do you think he will write a letter to the smiling lady in the paper? Why or why not?

_____

_____

Dear Sheriff Bud,

2. Read to the end of page 21.
What two things did Henry decide not to do?

_____

_____

What was Henry's inspiration?

_____

_____

_____

Why did he think this would work?

_____

_____

_____

3. Read to the end of the story.
Draw a picture that shows how Henry solved his problem. Then answer these questions.

Do you think Henry's letter was a good idea? Why or why not?

_____

_____

_____

Now look back at the predictions you made at the beginning of the story. Did your predictions agree with what you read? Explain.

_____

_____

_____

Who Made You Laugh? 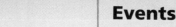 Which character did you think was funniest? What did he or she do to make you feel that way?

_____

_____

_____

_____

Writing About the Story Write some notes about these four parts of the story.

Characters

Events

Problem

Ending

In a small group, talk about the part of the story you like the most.

Making Inferences About Characters Work
with a partner to complete the chart.

A. What Henry Is Like	How Can You Tell?
_____	_____
_____	_____
_____	_____
_____	_____

B. What Henry Feels	How Can You Tell?
At the beginning of the story:	
_____	_____
_____	_____
_____	_____
While he is trying to figure out what to do:	
_____	_____
_____	_____
_____	_____
After the second Sheriff Bud show:	
_____	_____
_____	_____
_____	_____

Artful Advertisements Sheriff Bud used words like *positively guaranteed* and *chockfull of energy* for his commercials. What words would you use if you wanted to persuade someone to buy something? Write an advertisement for a real product or for one you make up. Your product could be something to eat or drink, something to play with, or something for school. Use the space below to design your advertisement.

OTIS'S SCIENTIFIC EXPERIMENT

What's Good to Eat? Fill up the grocery carts on this page. In the **Good Food** cart, write in the names of some foods that are good for you. In the **Junk Food** cart, write the names of some foods that are not so good for you. If you want to, you can draw some pictures of the foods too.

GOOD FOOD   JUNK FOOD

The teacher did an **experiment** to prove that a small bag of marbles is heavier than a small bag of popcorn.

He put the popcorn on a **scale.** Then he slid the **weights** until the **scale** was balanced. The bag of popcorn weighed 21 **grams.**

He then put the bag of marbles on the scale. Even though the bag of popcorn is the same size as the bag of marbles, the marbles weigh much more.

Write the names of two different things you might weigh on a scale:

_____ _____. Use the two words you wrote and the words in dark type above to complete this paragraph. You will use some words more than once.

My _____ will prove that a _____ weighs more than a _____. I will use the _____ to weigh the _____ first. To find out how much it weighs I will slide the _____ until the scale is balanced. The numbers on the scale do not show pounds or ounces. They show _____. After I write down how many _____ the _____ weighs, I will weigh the _____. The one that weighs more _____ is heavier.

Preview and Predict  Otis Spofford is a boy who likes to stir up excitement. What do you think will happen with Otis and the scientific experiment? Preview the story and write what you predict will happen.

_____

_____

_____

_____

Reading Notes As you read, write down things you'd like to remember, such as funny events or interesting words.

_____

_____

_____

_____

_____

_____

_____

_____

_____

_____

_____

_____

_____

_____

_____

_____

Express Your Thoughts  Write what you thought about this story. You could write about one of these questions or one of your own questions.

• Did anything in the story surprise you? If so, what?

• Do you agree or disagree with what Otis did? Tell why.

• What did you think of the way the story ended?

_____

_____

_____

_____

_____

_____

_____

_____

What They Thought and How They Felt Work with two other classmates to play the parts of Otis Spofford, Ellen Tebbits, and Mrs. Gitler. Speaking as one of the characters, tell how you felt when each of these events happened:

• The experiment is announced.

• Mutt begins to look sick while Pinky grows healthy.

• Mrs. Gitler announces that the experiment is ruined.

• Ellen Tebbits confesses to feeding Mutt.

• Mrs. Gitler gives Mutt away.

Making Inferences About Events  Here are some things that happened in the story. Tell what caused the characters to feel or act the way they did.

Otis made a plan to feed Mutt during his lunch period. What caused him to make this plan?

Otis made the plan because

_____

_____

_____

_____

Ellen confessed that she had fed Mutt. What do you think caused Ellen to confess?

Ellen confessed because _____

_____

_____

_____

_____

Otis decided that Ellen wasn't so bad after all. What caused Otis to feel that way?

Otis felt that way because

_____

_____

_____

_____

Vitamins

100 TABLETS

Base Words and Word Parts 🐀 Read each sentence. Look for the base word and word parts in each word in dark type. Decide whether or not the base word changed spelling when the ending was added. Then fill out the chart. The first one has been done.

Sentence	Prefix	Base Word	Suffix or Ending	Spelling Change in Base Word
Otis **disliked** Stewy's idea about naming the rat Otis.	dis	like	ed	Yes. The final *e* was dropped.
The class laughed **loudly** at the joke.				
Finally, Mrs. Gitler **unlocked** the door.				
Watching Pinky eat made Otis even **hungrier**.				
Ellen sniffed **unhappily** as she told Mrs. Gitler about feeding Mutt.				

Action Words 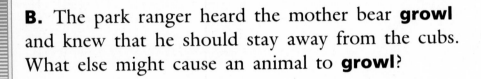 Read the sentences and answer the questions.

A. Otis was hungry. His stomach began to make a low, rolling sound. He was sure Mrs. Gitler would hear the **rumble**. What are two other things besides a stomach that might **rumble**?

_____

_____

B. The park ranger heard the mother bear **growl** and knew that he should stay away from the cubs. What else might cause an animal to **growl**?

_____

C. Raymond turned on the motor on the fish tank. Air began to bubble through the water, making a **gurgling** sound. Where else might you hear a

gurgling sound? _____

D. The rat put its nose on the cheese and drew in a quick, noisy breath. He **sniffed** again before taking a bite. Why do you think animals **sniff** food?

_____

THE HARD-BOILED EGG FAD

Fads, Fads, Fads Meet with a group to think of some fads. Write a fad in each box below. Then talk about each fad. Is it fun? Is it foolish? Would you describe it some other way, such as expensive or dangerous? Write what you think about each fad.

Fad: _____

Description: _____

_____

_____

_____

Fad: _____

Description: _____

_____

_____

_____

Fad: _____

Description: _____

_____

_____

_____

18

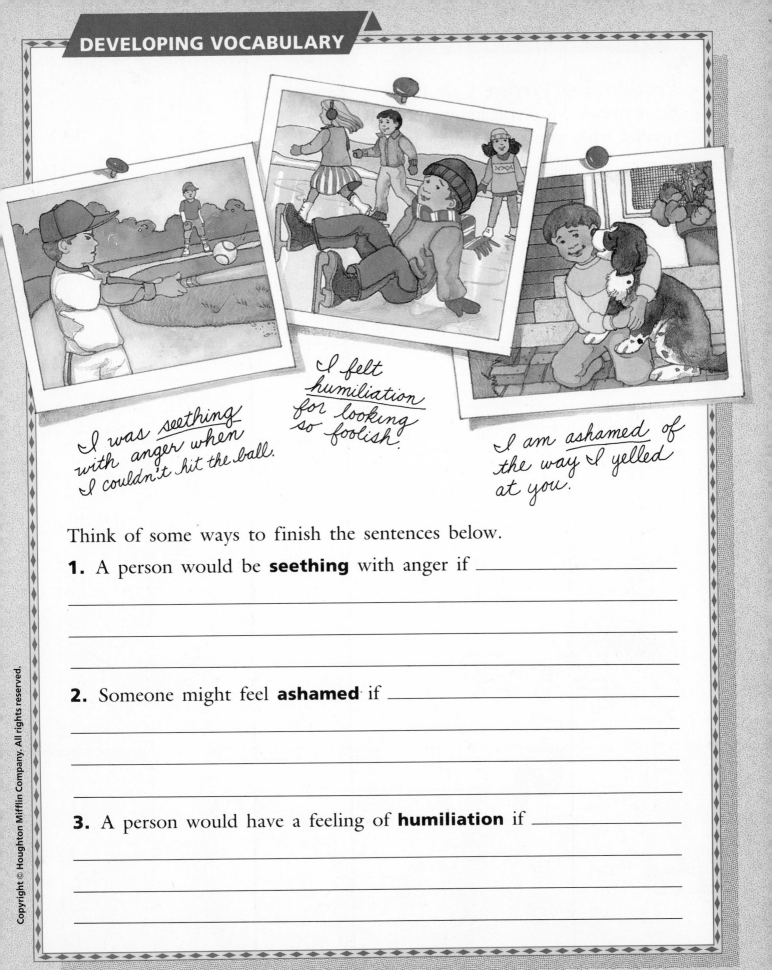

I was *seething* with anger when I couldn't hit the ball.

I felt *humiliation* for looking so foolish.

I am *ashamed* of the way I yelled at you.

Think of some ways to finish the sentences below.

1. A person would be **seething** with anger if _____

_____

_____

_____

2. Someone might feel **ashamed** if _____

_____

_____

_____

3. A person would have a feeling of **humiliation** if _____

_____

_____

_____

Preview and Predict Preview the story and think about what you know about Ramona. Then predict what you think might happen in the story.

_____

_____

_____

Reading Notes As you read, write down some things you want to remember.

_____

_____

_____

_____

_____

_____

_____

_____

_____

_____

_____

_____

_____

_____

Surprised? Did your predictions agree with what happened to Ramona? Or were you surprised by what happened? Tell what surprised you or didn't surprise you. Tell why you felt that way.

_____

_____

_____

_____

_____

_____

Just Add Boiling Water Fill in the hard-boiled eggs below with notes about the story. Work with a partner and take turns using your notes to discuss the story.

Setting

Characters

Major Events

Ending

Making Inferences ⬭ Go back to the story and be a character detective. Find out how Ramona felt at different times and fill out the detective's report with your information.

Go-Get-em **Detective Agency**

Detective (You): _____

Suspect Being Investigated:

Ramona Quimby

Suspect's Age: <u>8 years old</u>

1. When the hard-boiled egg fad was just getting started, how did Ramona feel? _____

_____

How can you tell? _____

_____

2. How did Ramona Quimby feel after she cracked the egg on her head?

_____

_____

3. What were Ramona's feelings after she overheard Mrs. Whaley talking about her? _____

_____

4. Did Ramona's feelings for Yard Ape change by the end of the story?

_____

How can you tell? _____

Base Words and Word Parts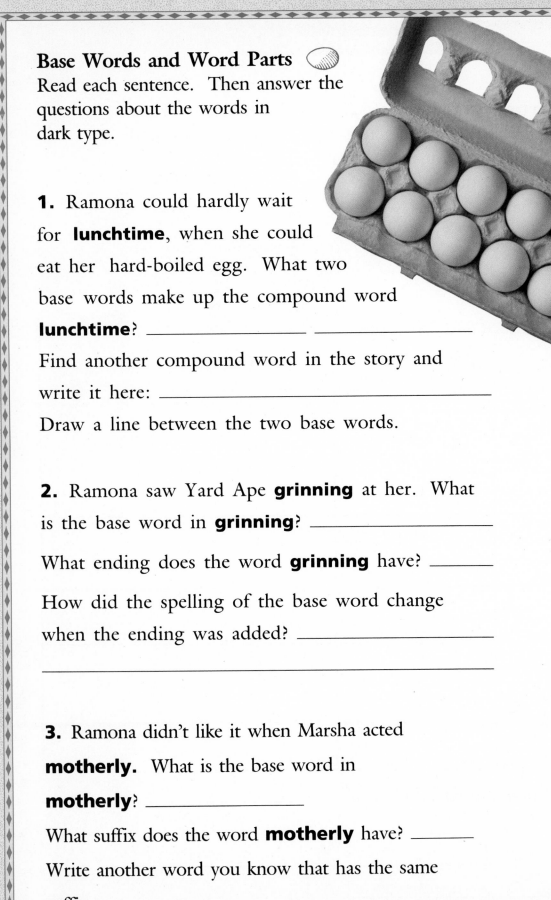

Read each sentence. Then answer the questions about the words in dark type.

1. Ramona could hardly wait for **lunchtime**, when she could eat her hard-boiled egg. What two base words make up the compound word **lunchtime**? _____ _____

Find another compound word in the story and write it here: _____

Draw a line between the two base words.

2. Ramona saw Yard Ape **grinning** at her. What is the base word in **grinning**? _____

What ending does the word **grinning** have? _____

How did the spelling of the base word change when the ending was added? _____

_____

3. Ramona didn't like it when Marsha acted **motherly.** What is the base word in **motherly**? _____

What suffix does the word **motherly** have? _____

Write another word you know that has the same suffix. _____

Charting the Stories Fill in the chart below to tell about the characters and major events in each of the stories you read. Then answer the question below the chart.

Story	Characters	Major Events
Henry Writes a Letter		
Otis's Scientific Experiment		
The Hard-boiled Egg Fad		

What makes these stories seem real? _____

_____

_____

_____

A Theme PROJECT

Take a Poll of Favorite Authors

Choosing and Planning

Beverly Cleary is the favorite author of many readers. Who are your classmates' favorite authors? As a group project, take a poll to find the answer.

Think for a moment about books you have read that you enjoyed. Who wrote them? Write their names. Work with the group to add other names.

> When you take a poll, you ask the same questions of different people. You find out the opinions of a group.

1. *Beverly Cleary* _____
2. _____
3. _____
4. _____
5. _____
6. _____
7. _____
8. _____
9. _____
10. _____

To complete this project, you and your group will need to take these steps:

> You may want to go to the library. Ask the librarian for help in adding names.

- Think of questions to ask in your poll.
- Decide who will be polled and who will ask the questions.
- Gather the information.
- Show the information in a table.
- Think of a way to share your results.

Write a few questions that can be answered with one of the names on your list.

Examples: Which author do you like best? Which author's books are the funniest?

Other possible questions:

_____

_____

_____

_____

_____

You might want to ask a more open-ended question too.

Example: Why is that author your favorite?

Other possible open-ended questions:

_____

_____

_____

_____

Talk with other group members about all of your questions. Which ones seem best for your poll? Also make these decisions:

- Whom do you want to poll? Other students in your grade? Students in the upper and lower grades?

- Who will ask the questions? Each poll-taker will need copies of the questions. What information should be on each sheet of questions?

Checkpoint

My assignment is to _____

To complete my assignment, I will need to _____

_____

_____

Putting It Together

When all the poll-takers have done their jobs, collect the questions and answers. One way to show the results is in a table.

PROJECT POINTER: A Table

A table shows facts in easy-to-read rows and columns. The lines that go across form rows. The lines that go up and down form columns. A title tells what information the table gives.

In this table, there are captions across the top and along the left side. The side captions are the names of the authors. The captions across the top are key words from the questions asked in the poll.

To place authors' last names in alphabetical order:

- Look at the first letter of each name. Decide which of those letters come first in the alphabet.
- When the first letters are the same, use the second letter of each name.
- When the first two letters are the same, use the third letter of each name.

Authors: Third Grade Opinions

	Favorite Author	Most Unusual Characters
Cleary, Beverly	7	5
Dalgliesh, Alice	4	2
dePaola, Tomie	8	4

27

What else would you like to include in your table? Write some ideas here. Talk about all your ideas. Then work together to make your table.

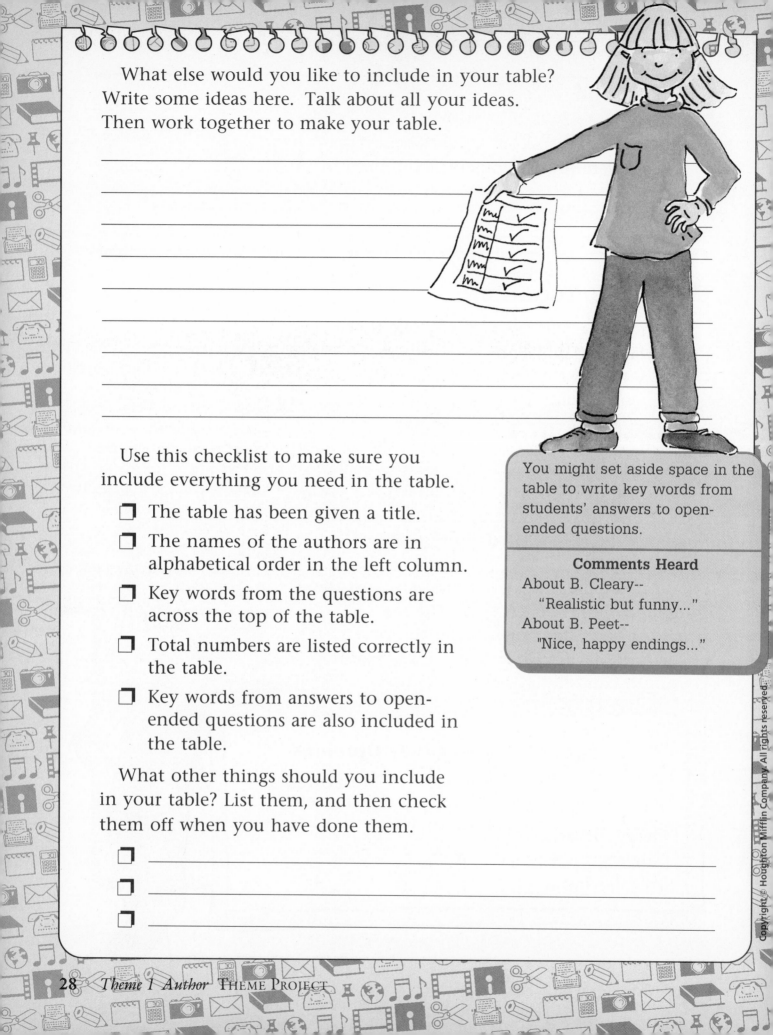

_____
_____
_____
_____
_____
_____
_____

Use this checklist to make sure you include everything you need in the table.

❏ The table has been given a title.

❏ The names of the authors are in alphabetical order in the left column.

❏ Key words from the questions are across the top of the table.

❏ Total numbers are listed correctly in the table.

❏ Key words from answers to open-ended questions are also included in the table.

What other things should you include in your table? List them, and then check them off when you have done them.

❏ _____

❏ _____

❏ _____

You might set aside space in the table to write key words from students' answers to open-ended questions.

Comments Heard
About B. Cleary--
   "Realistic but funny..."
About B. Peet--
   "Nice, happy endings..."

Presenting the Project

Look at all the information in your completed table: the numbers, the totals, any comments you have included. What summarizing statements can you make about your results?

How will you display the results of your poll? Think about these ideas:

> To **summarize**, state the important points in just a few sentences:
> The favorite Grade 3 author is... The author who has made the most of us laugh is ...

- Write an article for the school newspaper. In the first paragraph, tell who was polled, who took the poll, and where and when it was taken. In the rest of the article, explain the reasons for taking the poll and give the results.

- Make a poster. Include a bar graph showing the results of the poll. Display the poster on a bulletin board in your classroom, in the school library, or in the local library.

- Write a letter to the school or local librarian to report the results of the poll. Suggest that the librarian use the results to help decide which books to buy.

Other ideas for presenting the results of the poll:

_____

_____

_____

_____

_____

_____

My Own Project Plan

Plan your own project. Use the ideas that come to you when you read the stories in "Beverly Cleary." Decide first if you will work alone or with others. Then use this sheet to make a plan.

Exploring Ideas

What things would you like to learn about? List as many ideas as you can think of:

_____   _____

_____   _____

Choose the best idea: _____

Give one reason why that topic is a good choice: _____

_____

Gathering Information

Where will you find the information you want? Check the sources you will use.

❑ Encyclopedias   ❑ Nonfiction books

❑ Magazines

❑ Other _____

Presenting Your Project

How will you share what you have learned? Check the project you will do.

❑ Written report   ❑ Speech   ❑ Model

❑ Poster

❑ Other _____

Writing a Realistic Story

Prewriting

Beverly Cleary writes stories about ordinary children
who face real-life problems. So can you. Write
names for several imaginary characters like the
characters found in Beverly Cleary's stories.

_____

_____

Choose the two names that sound the most like
characters you'd like to put into a story.
Then draw a star next to those names.

Think about some problems your characters might try to
solve. Write your ideas under the heading marked *Problems*
below. Then, with a partner or in a group, think of solutions
to the problems. Write the solutions on the right.

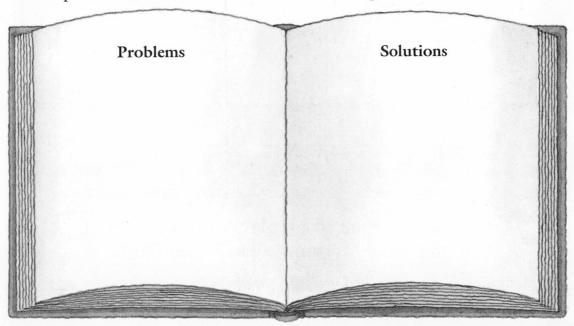

Problems	Solutions

Choosing a Topic   Think about these questions.

- Who will be reading my story?
- Which problem would make the most interesting story?

Choose the problem you will write about.
Complete this sentence:

I will write about _____

Exploring Your Topic   Now you can plan the parts of your story. Use the chart below to write what will happen to the main characters.

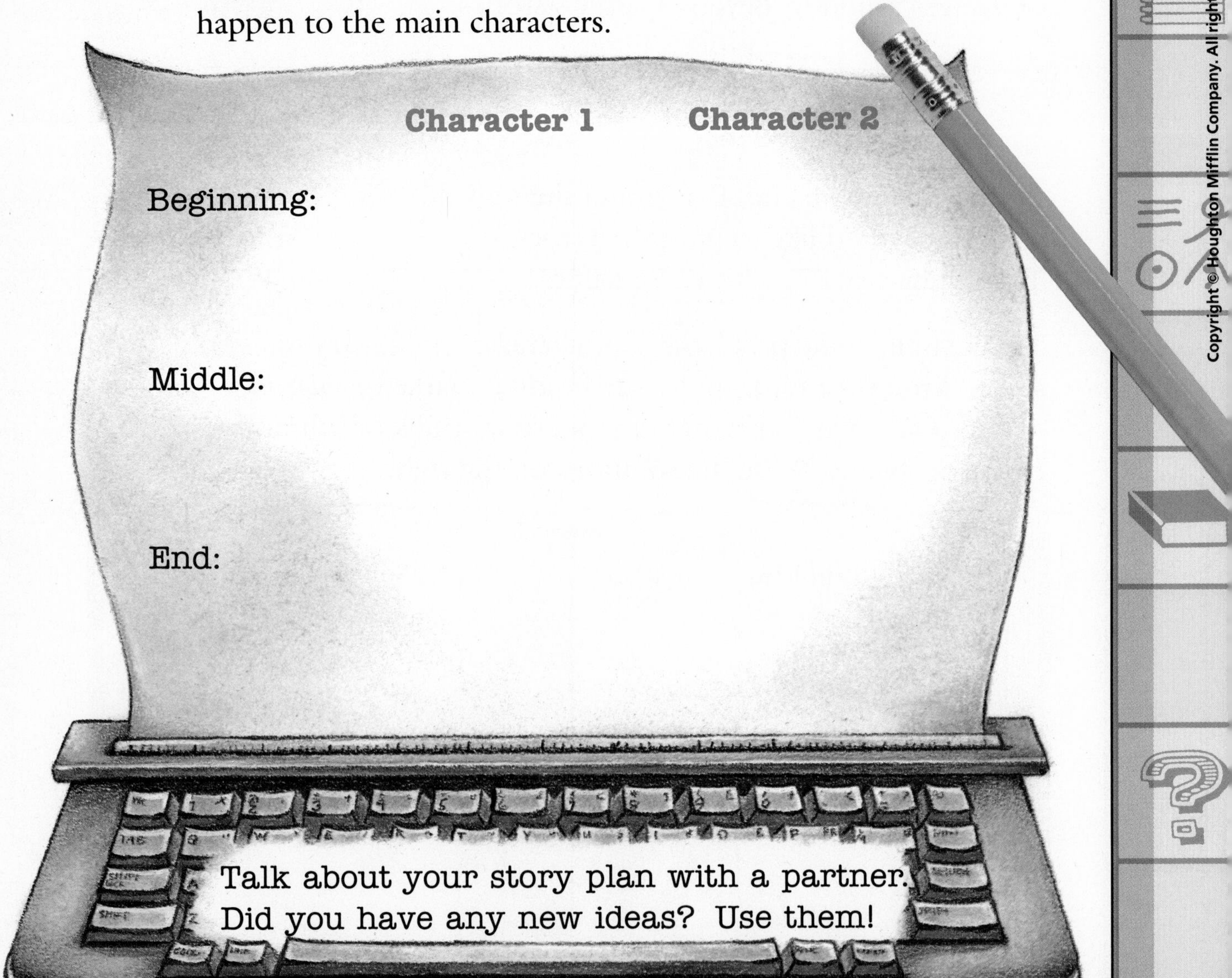

	Character 1	Character 2
Beginning:		
Middle:		
End:		

Talk about your story plan with a partner.
Did you have any new ideas? Use them!

Drafting

Now it is time to begin writing. Using a separate sheet of paper, write as much as you can. Don't worry about making mistakes, because you can correct them later. It may help you to keep this question in mind as you write.

- What details can I use to make the story seem as if it really happened?

Revising

Read the first draft of your story. Did you tell enough? Where could you add more details and exact words? Make your changes.

Writing Conference Now that you have looked over your work, work with a group to make more changes. Read your story to the group and use the questions below to discuss your story.

Questions for a Conference

- Do the characters seem real?
- Does the order of events make sense?
- Does the story have a good ending?

Make any changes that you think will improve your story.

Proofreading

To help you to check your story for mistakes, use the Proofreading Checklist below.

Proofreading Checklist
☐ Did I begin and end each sentence correctly?
☐ Does each sentence tell a complete thought?
☐ Did I spell all of the words correctly?

Make sure you have capitalized all proper nouns in your story. This chart will help you to recognize proper nouns.

Proper Nouns
A **proper noun** is the name of a person, place, or thing.

person	place	thing
Mrs. Santos	New York	Liberty Bell

Publishing

Now copy your story neatly and add a title. Think of a way to share your story. Here are two ideas.

- Draw pictures and make a cover for your story.
- Make your story into a play. Have your classmates act out the play.

Write your own ideas for sharing.

_____

_____

_____

Writer's Log What have you learned about writing a story? Write your thoughts on a separate sheet of paper.

Mysteries of the DEEP

License to Explore

Underwater Explorer

Date I Dive Into Theme

Date I Come Up For Air

Exploration Goals

 Read about three different mysteries of the deep

 Learn how to read and understand informational selections

 Read other nonfiction books and write about a favorite topic

 Make an underwater diorama

 Write a report and choose other writing activities to do

BOOKS I WANT TO READ

_____
_____
_____
_____
_____
_____
_____
_____
_____
_____
_____

BOOK-SHARING
I D E A S

◆ **Make a Map** Make a map that shows the undersea location of a mystery of the deep. Show your map to the class.

◆ **Be a Television Reporter** Present a TV news report to your class about an undersea exploration you have read about.

MY WRITING IDEAS

_____
_____
_____
_____
_____
_____
_____
_____

Mysteries of the Deep

Exploring the Deep Imagine that you are a famous underwater explorer. What kinds of mysterious or surprising things do you think you might find in the ocean? Add your ideas to the octopus below.

After you have finished reading "Mysteries of the Deep," come back to this octopus. Add anything new that you have discovered in your reading. Also add any ideas that your reading gave you about mysteries you would like to explore. Write your ideas on the octopus and in the water around it.

THE *TITANIC*: LOST... AND FOUND

An Imaginary Voyage 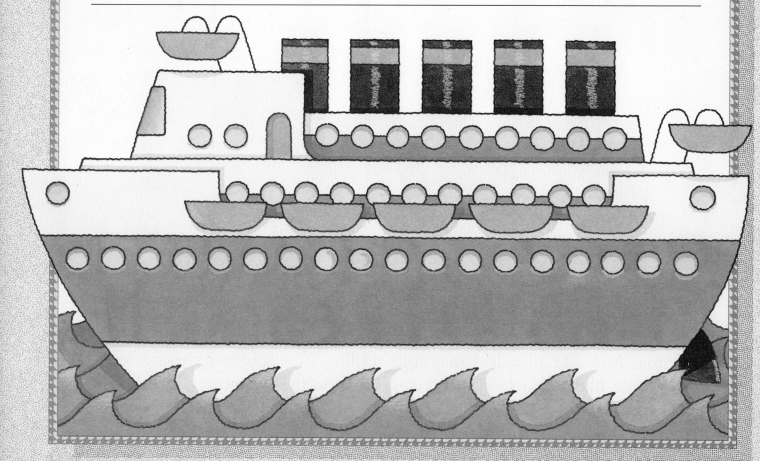 Imagine that you are
going to take a trip on this ocean liner. What are
some of the interesting things you would want to
do and see?

_____

_____

_____

_____

_____

_____

_____

_____

Look at the picture and read the sentences. Then answer the question on each card.

Experts

Experts know a lot about special subjects. What would you ask a ship **expert** before sailing on a ship?

_____

_____

_____

Signal

The captain saw a **signal** that told him the other ship was in danger. What is an example of a **signal** that could be seen from far away?

_____

_____

_____

Compartments

A ship has different **compartments** to keep things separated. Why would you keep food and medicine in different **compartments**?

_____

_____

_____

Survivors

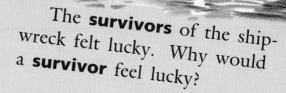

The **survivors** of the ship-wreck felt lucky. Why would a **survivor** feel lucky?

_____

_____

_____

Using the Preview and Self-Question

Strategy 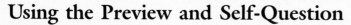 Preview *The* Titanic: *Lost . . . and Found* by reading the titles of the sections, looking at the pictures, and reading the captions. What would you like to find out when you read the selection? Write one or two questions that you think the selection will answer.

_____

_____

_____

_____

Reading Notes As you read, write down any thoughts or information you would like to remember. If you find answers to any questions you wrote above, write the answers here. You may also want to write words that describe the *Titanic,* and other interesting words you come across.

_____

_____

_____

_____

_____

_____

_____

Share Your Feelings Was there one part of the selection about the *Titanic* that caused you to have strong feelings? Here are some parts you might remember:

- There were not enough lifeboats on the *Titanic*.
- The *Californian* did not come to help the *Titanic*.
- The band was playing as the ship went down.

Write how you felt about one of these events, or about any other part of the story you choose.

_____

_____

_____

_____

_____

_____

_____

_____

TITANIC SINKS! MANY LIVES LOST!

The *Titanic* Sinks!

Imagine that you are back in the year 1912. Work with a group of classmates to write a news story about the sinking of the *Titanic*. In your news story, include quotes from an interview with a ship-builder, a survivor, and a rescuer. Be sure your news story answers these questions: *Who* was there? *What* happened? *When* and *Where* did it happen? and *Why* did it happen?

Main Ideas and Supporting Details With a partner, look back at *The* Titanic: *Lost . . . and Found.* Write one main idea and some supporting details for each part of the selection. The first one has been started for you.

1. The Wonder Ship

Main Idea: The *Titanic* was the biggest, fanciest, and "safest" ship the world had ever seen.

Details: The ship was four city blocks long and as tall as an eleven-story building; it was a floating palace, with restaurants, a post office, a gym, and fancy rooms. It had _____

_____

_____

_____

_____

_____

2. Iceberg

Main Idea: _____

_____

_____

Details: _____

_____

_____

_____

_____

_____

3. Never Again

Main Idea: _____

_____

_____

Details: _____

_____

_____

_____

_____

_____

4. Found at Last

Main Idea: _____

_____

_____

Details: _____

_____

_____

_____

_____

_____

_____

_____

_____

All Aboard 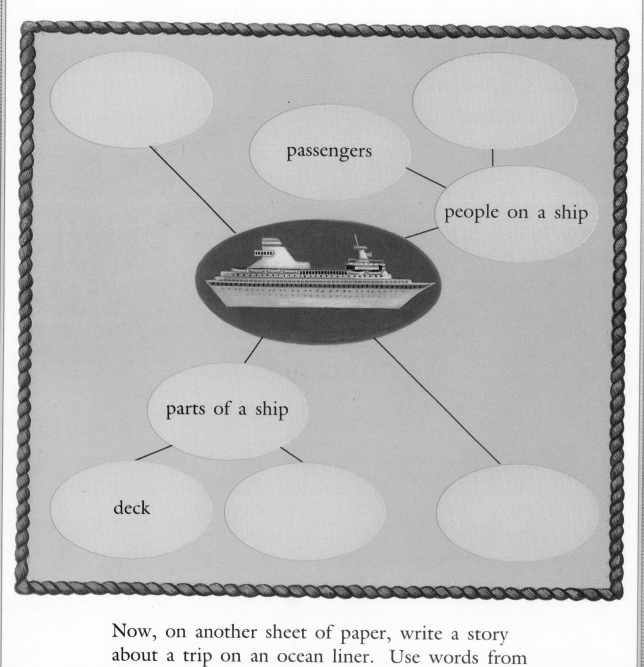 *The* Titanic: *Lost . . . and Found* included many words that have to do with ships. Add some of those words as well as others you know to the word web below. Look back at the selection if you want to.

passengers

people on a ship

parts of a ship

deck

Now, on another sheet of paper, write a story about a trip on an ocean liner. Use words from your word web in your story.

Preview and Self-Question Preview the selection. Think about what you would expect to learn from reading this selection. Write the questions you expect to have answered.

_____

_____

_____

_____

_____

_____

Reading Notes As you read, write down any answers you find to your questions. Also write down any new questions you think of.

_____

_____

_____

_____

_____

_____

_____

_____

_____

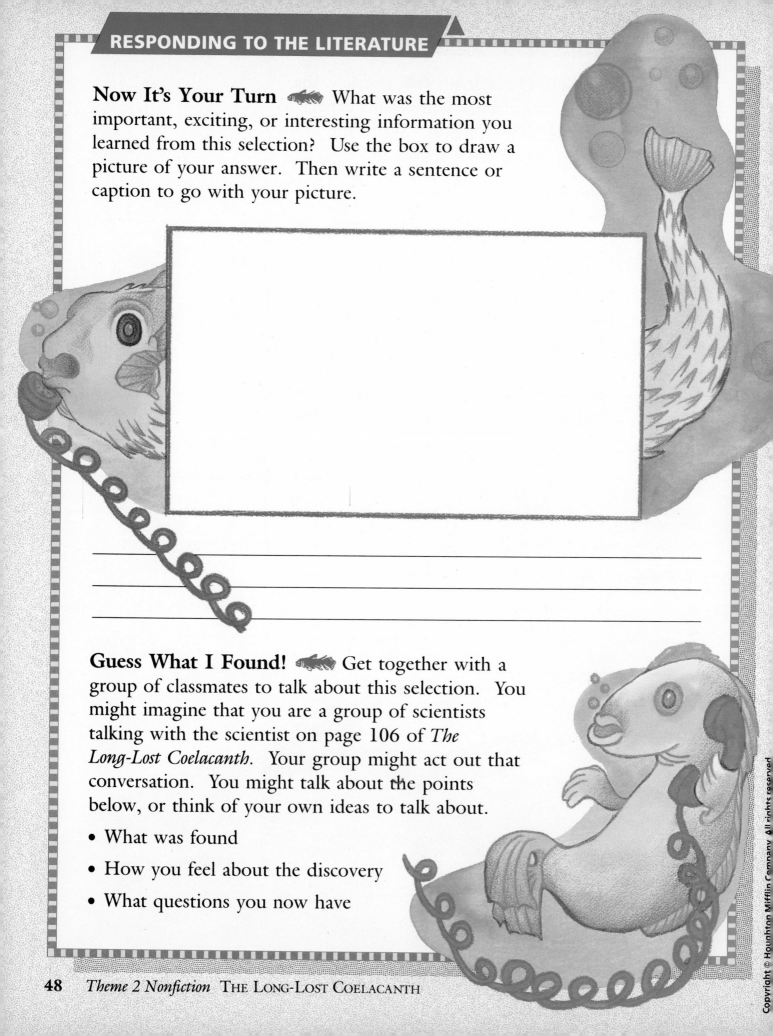

Now It's Your Turn What was the most important, exciting, or interesting information you learned from this selection? Use the box to draw a picture of your answer. Then write a sentence or caption to go with your picture.

Guess What I Found! Get together with a group of classmates to talk about this selection. You might imagine that you are a group of scientists talking with the scientist on page 106 of *The Long-Lost Coelacanth*. Your group might act out that conversation. You might talk about the points below, or think of your own ideas to talk about.

- What was found
- How you feel about the discovery
- What questions you now have

Topic, Main Ideas, and Supporting Details

Think about the topic of *The Long-Lost Coelacanth,* and write it below. Then complete each part by finishing the main ideas and adding supporting details.

Topic: _____

Main Idea: A kind of fish called the coelacanth was thought to be extinct until _____

_____

Supporting Details: _____

_____

_____

Main Idea: The whole world was excited by the discovery of _____

Supporting Details: _____

_____

_____

_____

Main Idea: Unlike coelacanths, their "relatives" the rhipidistians have slowly _____

_____

Supporting Details: _____

_____

_____

_____

Main Idea: The coelacanth helped scientists learn _____

_____

Supporting Details: _____

_____

_____

_____

Summarizing 🐟 Use the main ideas from these pages to write a summary of the selection. Retell the important points as briefly as you can, but be sure your summary makes sense!

_____

_____

_____

_____

_____

_____

_____

Technical Words Sometimes the meanings of technical words are important for understanding what you are reading. Think about any important technical words you have come across in *The Long-Lost Coelacanth* and in your independent reading. Write those words and their meanings on the lines below. Then share them with a partner, explaining why the meanings were important to understanding the selection and how you figured them out.

_____

_____

_____

_____

_____

_____

_____

_____

_____

_____

_____

_____

_____

_____

_____

_____

_____

_____

Discovering the Past What object or animal from the past would you like to discover? Draw a picture of your surprising discovery.

Now write about what you have found.

_____

_____

_____

_____

_____

THE LOCH NESS MONSTER

Three Mysterious Shapes Suppose you saw these three shapes in the water. What would you think you were seeing? Draw what you think you would see below the water.

Now write a few sentences explaining your drawing.

_____

_____

_____

_____

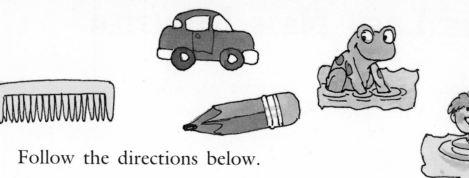

Follow the directions below.

Draw a circle around the **creatures.**

Name some other creatures. _____

_____

Put an X on the **mammal.**

Write the names of some other mammals. _____

_____

Underline where you might read a **legend.**

What is the difference between a legend and a fact? _____

_____

Draw a picture of a **genuine** animal.

Now write a sentence using two of these words:
creatures, mammals, legends, and *genuine.*

_____

_____

_____

REAL?
MONSTER?
MAKE-BELIEVE?

Preview and Self-Question Preview the selection. What do you expect to find out about the Loch Ness Monster? Write the questions you expect to be answered.

_____

_____

_____

_____

_____

_____

Reading Notes As you are reading, write down the answers to your questions. Also write any other questions that you think of as you read.

_____

_____

_____

_____

_____

_____

_____

_____

_____

_____

In Your Opinion After reading this selection, do you believe there is a Loch Ness Monster? Give reasons for your answer.

_____

_____

_____

_____

_____

_____

_____

Giant Questions Look back at the questions and answers you wrote on Journal page 55. Meet with a small group to talk about the Loch Ness Monster. Bring your questions and answers to the discussion.

Main Ideas and Supporting Details

Write details to support these main ideas.

A. Main Idea

People have described Nessie in many different ways.

Supporting Details

1. _____

2. _____

B. Main Idea

Scientists have different ideas about what the Loch Ness Monster might be.

Supporting Details

1. _____

2. _____

Find one more main idea in the selection. Write it here:

_____

_____

Now use these main ideas and others you talked about to write a short summary of *The Loch Ness Monster*.

_____

_____

_____

_____

_____

_____

Monster Impostors 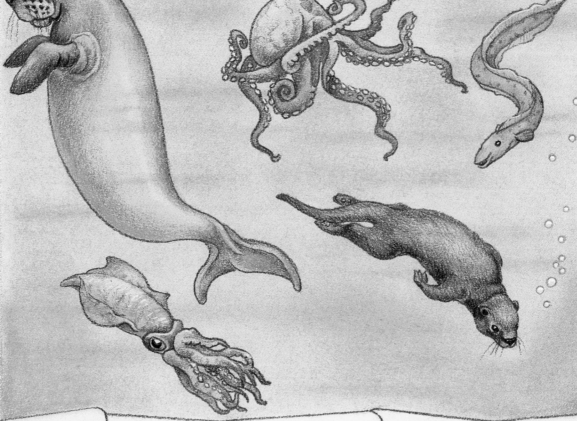 Read the information on each card. Then draw a line from each card to the animal in the aquarium named on the card.

After you've sorted them out, decide which animal interests you the most. Find information about that animal in an encyclopedia. Then, on another sheet of paper, use the facts you have learned to make a poster about your animal.

SEA COW
A mammal with flippers and whiskers

OCTOPUS
A sea animal that has eight arms

OTTER
An animal with webbed toes, claws, and thick fur

EEL
A long fish shaped like a snake

SQUID
A long sea animal with ten arms

A Theme PROJECT

Underwater Diorama

Choosing and Planning

Make an underwater diorama to show life in the deep. You will be answering these questions:

- What body of water do I want to learn about?
- What is the best way to gather information?
- How can I present the information I find?

Decide if you want to work alone or with a partner. Then start to explore some topics. The library card catalog or computer catalog will show you what nonfiction books have been written on your topic.

To find the nonfiction books you need, look in the card catalog. You would look up the subject *Oceans* to find titles of books about oceans. Call numbers appear on the left of the cards. They will help you find the books.

- Glance through several nonfiction books on life in rivers, lakes, ponds, and oceans.
- Pick one or two that have detailed underwater scenes.
- Choose an underwater scene to show in a diorama.

Checkpoint

The scene I/we chose to make is _____

The reason I/we chose this scene is _____

_____

Putting It Together

Now that you have chosen your scene, start to gather information about the plant and animal life that you will include in your diorama.

- Look in an encyclopedia.
- Scan nonfiction books.

Take notes to help you remember the information. Write only enough words to help you remember the important facts.

Sample notes:

What plants grow in and around a pond?

water lilies   **cattails**
bur reed   **water willow**
saw grass

World Book Encyclopedia, Ponds

Steps for Scanning

- Think of key words, such as *reed, plant,* or *cattail,* to help you find the information you need.
- When you find the information you need, read slowly and carefully to get the facts right.

The next step is to make the diorama. Here is a checklist to make sure you don't forget anything:

- ❏ I/We have decided what plants and animals to include.
- ❏ I/We have collected enough information.
- ❏ I/We have made a sketch of everything in the scene.
- ❏ I/We have all the art supplies and other materials needed.

Presenting the Project

Think of an interesting way to present your diorama. Here are two suggestions. Check the idea you like best, or make up your own.

> To summarize, tell the important points or facts in a few sentences.

> 1. A cattail has long leaves like straps. Its head is shaped like a cylinder and is made up of small brown flowers.
> 2. A water lily has floating leaves and white and pink flowers.

❏ A Fact Sheet

Number each plant or animal in the diorama, or make a simple drawing of each thing on a sheet of paper. Summarize the information about each plant or animal. Write your summaries beside numbers or beside the drawings.

Other ideas: _____

❏ An Oral Presentation

Look through your notecards to find interesting facts. Plan the order in which you will tell things. Arrange your notecards in order, and use the notes to help you remember what to say. Speak slowly and clearly.

Other ideas: _____

An Idea of My Own: _____

_____

A Description of How I Will Do It:

_____

_____

_____

My Own Project Plan

Plan your own project. Use the ideas that come to you when you read "Mysteries of the Deep." Decide first if you will work alone or with others. Then use this sheet to make the plan.

Exploring Ideas

What things would you like to learn about? List as many ideas as you can think of:

_____

_____

_____

Choose the best idea: _____

Give one reason why that topic is a good choice: _____

_____

Gathering Information

Where will you find the information you want? Check the sources you will use.

❏ Encyclopedias   ❏ Nonfiction books

❏ Magazines

❏ Other _____

Presenting Your Project

How will you share what you have learned? Check the project you will do.

❏ Written report   ❏ Speech   ❏ Model

❏ Poster

❏ Other _____

Writing a Research Report

Prewriting

Get ready to dive for a report topic! Write the names of some undersea topics you would like to know about.

_____

_____

_____

If you are interested in another topic, write it here.

_____

Choosing a Topic Look at your topic ideas. Answer these questions.

- For whom am I writing my report?
- What would my readers like to learn?
- Can I find information on the topic?
- Is the topic too big to cover in one report?
- Would one part of my topic make a better report?

Talk with a partner about your topic ideas to help you to decide which you will write about. Circle it.

Exploring Your Topic Write three questions you would like to answer in your report.

1. _____

2. _____

3. _____

Talk about your report plans with a partner to get new ideas. Use any of these new ideas that you like.

Look in reference books for answers to the questions you wrote down above. Take notes, like the ones shown on the card below. When you write your report, your questions will be your topic sentences. The answers will be the supporting details.

> ### Note Card
>
> - How does the cuttlefish protect itself?
>   - Detail: changes color to hide itself
>   - Detail: shoots ink to scare attackers
>   - Source: *Mysteries and Marvels of Ocean Life*
>   by Rick Morris

Drafting

As you write your first draft on a separate sheet of paper, do not stop to correct mistakes. You can make changes later. These questions might help you as you work on your first draft.

- What do I want my reader to learn?
- How much detail should I include?

Revising

Read your report and think about your work. Can you add more facts? Make any other changes you think are necessary.

Writing Conference Meet with your group to read and discuss your report. During your discussion, you may want to ask these questions.

Questions for a Conference

- Does the report give enough facts?
- Is any information missing?
- Do I need to explain any facts?

Make changes that will make your report clear and complete.

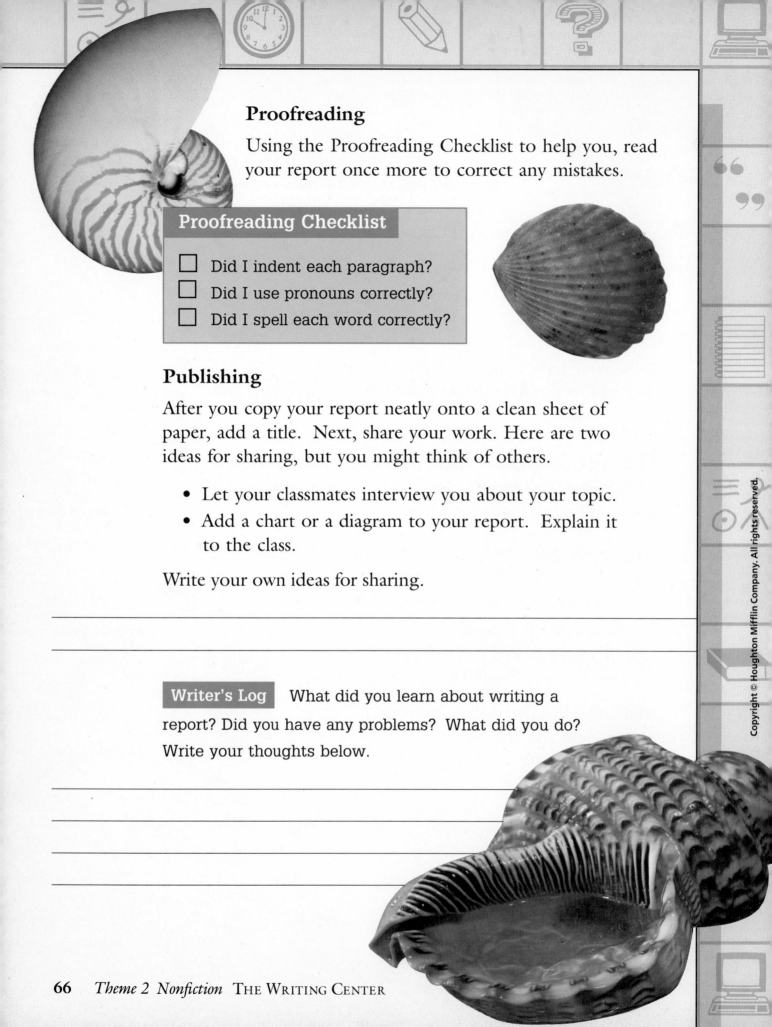

Proofreading

Using the Proofreading Checklist to help you, read your report once more to correct any mistakes.

Proofreading Checklist

☐ Did I indent each paragraph?

☐ Did I use pronouns correctly?

☐ Did I spell each word correctly?

Publishing

After you copy your report neatly onto a clean sheet of paper, add a title. Next, share your work. Here are two ideas for sharing, but you might think of others.

- Let your classmates interview you about your topic.
- Add a chart or a diagram to your report. Explain it to the class.

Write your own ideas for sharing.

_____

_____

Writer's Log What did you learn about writing a report? Did you have any problems? What did you do? Write your thoughts below.

_____

_____

_____

_____

ONCE UPON A TIME

Passport to Other Lands

_____

_____
NAME

_____
DATE JOURNEY BEGINS

_____
DATE JOURNEY ENDS

On My Journey I Will

- ❂ Read three fairy tales from around the world
- ❂ Recognize how fairy tales from different cultures are often alike
- ❂ Choose books and writing projects to work on independently
- ❂ Make a fairy tale map
- ❂ Write a fairy tale

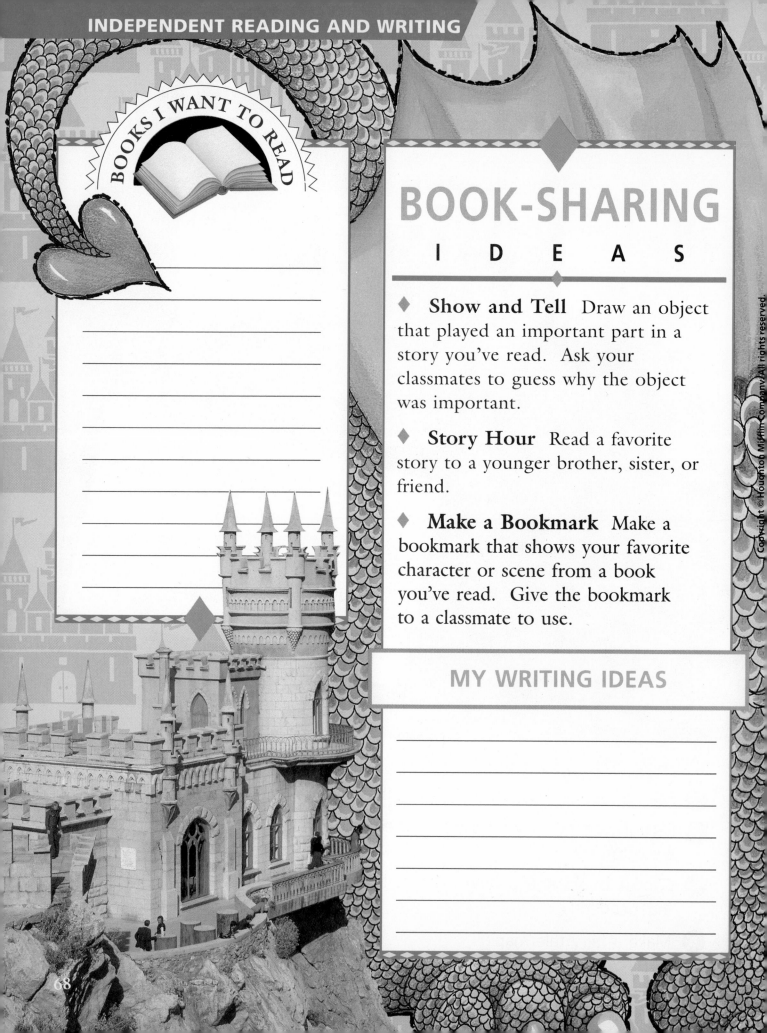

BOOKS I WANT TO READ

BOOK-SHARING
I D E A S

◆ **Show and Tell** Draw an object that played an important part in a story you've read. Ask your classmates to guess why the object was important.

◆ **Story Hour** Read a favorite story to a younger brother, sister, or friend.

◆ **Make a Bookmark** Make a bookmark that shows your favorite character or scene from a book you've read. Give the bookmark to a classmate to use.

MY WRITING IDEAS

Fairy Tales Are Made Of . . . Think about fairy tales you have read or heard. On the lines below, write some words that tell about the places, people, and things found in fairy tales.

Fairy Tale Places

Fairy Tale People

Magical Characters, Animals, and Objects

After you have finished reading "Once Upon a Time," come back to this page and add more words.

YEH-SHEN

In a Land Far Away  *Yeh-Shen* is a fairy tale set in China. Think of everything you know about China and write it down in the space on the fan.

Words of Feeling Read each sentence and put a check mark next to the correct answer. Then explain why you chose that answer.

What could make someone feel **sorrow**?

_____ going to an exciting new place

_____ leaving a favorite place forever

Why? _____

_____

_____

What could make someone feel **dread**?

_____ sitting down to eat a good meal

_____ going into a dark, spooky cave

Why? _____

_____

What could make someone feel **displeasure**?

_____ meeting a friend

_____ having someone lose your favorite book

Why? _____

_____

Reading Notes As you read *Yeh-Shen,* use this page to record the reading strategies you used, new words, and important questions or events you may wish to discuss later.

_____

_____

_____

_____

_____

_____

_____

_____

_____

_____

_____

_____

_____

_____

_____

_____

_____

_____

_____

_____

_____

_____

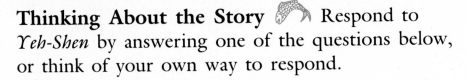

Thinking About the Story 🌾 Respond to
Yeh-Shen by answering one of the questions below,
or think of your own way to respond.

• Did *Yeh-Shen* remind you of another fairy tale?
How?

• How did you feel about the way the pages of the
story looked?

• Would you change the ending? How?

_____

_____

_____

_____

_____

_____

_____

_____

_____

_____

_____

Presenting a Play 🌾 With a group of classmates, select a scene from *Yeh-Shen* and turn it into
a play. Think about and plan what the characters
will say and do. Act out your scene for another
group.

Thinking About the Theme Answer the questions below.

What kind of character is Yeh-Shen? _____

_____

_____

_____

What kind of character is the stepmother? _____

_____

_____

_____

What happens to Yeh-Shen at the end of the story?

_____

_____

_____

_____

What do you think the theme of this story is?

_____

_____

_____

_____

Here, Kitty Kitty  Imagine what it would be like to have a magical pet. Think of an animal that could be your closest friend as well as a magical helper. On the hat below, draw a picture of your animal.

Now write a few sentences telling how your pet could use its magical powers to help you.

_____

_____

_____

_____

_____

_____

THE RAINBOW-COLORED HORSE

An Island Named "The Rich Port" The fairy tale *Yeh-Shen* is set in China. This next fairy tale is set in Puerto Rico. What do you know about Puerto Rico? Maybe more than you think! With a partner, write what you know about this island. Tell about its people, language, food, or anything else you know about it.

Read this story. Then complete each sentence below and answer the question that follows.

Ana and her dog had traveled a long way to bring a message to King Louis. But the gatekeeper would not let them into the kingdom. Suddenly, Ana's dog became **enchanted.** He began singing and dancing. While the gatekeeper watched the dog, Ana slipped through the gate and delivered her message. Working together, Ana and her magical dog had **outwitted** the gatekeeper.

You know Ana's dog was enchanted because it could _____

_____

_____

What is something else that an enchanted dog might do? _____

_____

_____

Ana and her dog outwitted the gatekeeper by _____

_____

_____

What is another way that Ana and her dog might have outwitted the gatekeeper?

_____

_____

_____

Using the Reading Strategies  Using the Preview and Predict Strategy, look at the illustrations and think about the title. What animal do you think will be magical? What magical things might that animal do?

_____
_____
_____
_____
_____

Now read to the end of page 164. Remember to use the Reading New Words Strategy if you come across a new word you don't understand. When you have finished, return to this page and answer the questions below.

What did Pío do when he guarded the maize field?

_____
_____
_____

What did Pío see at the maize field? _____

_____
_____

Think about what you have read. Change or add to your predictions if you wish. _____

_____

_____

Read to the end of page 168 to see if your predictions agree with what you read. Then answer the questions below.

What did Pío do in Don Nicanor's test?

_____

_____

_____

How well do you think Pío will do in the next two days of the contest?

_____

_____

_____

Finish reading the story. As you read, keep in mind your last prediction. If you come to a part of the story that you don't understand, use the Stop and Think Strategy. When you've finished, follow the directions below.

Tell what happened after Pío took the test and how the story ended. _____

_____

_____

Use the Summarizing Stories Strategy to think about the important parts of the story. Then tell the story to a friend.

Your Turn Write what you thought about the story and *Yeh-Shen*. You can answer one of the questions below, or you can write about something else.

- Which fairy tale did you like best? Why?
- Who was your favorite magical character? Why?
- How are the two endings different?

_____

_____

_____

_____

_____

_____

_____

Discussing the Three Brothers Carlos and Pedro were greedy and mean. Pío was kind and clever. Get together with a group and discuss what each character did or said that showed what kind of person he was.

Comparing and Contrasting  Answer these questions.

How are Pío and Yeh-Shen alike?

_____

_____

_____

_____

How are Carlos and Pedro like Yeh-Shen's stepmother?

_____

_____

_____

_____

What happens to Pío at the end of the story?

_____

_____

_____

_____

What is the theme of *The Rainbow-Colored Horse*?

_____

_____

Say What You Mean 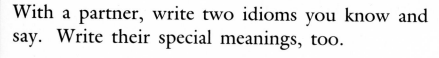 In *The Rainbow-Colored Horse* there are many idioms. An idiom is a group of words that has its own special meaning. Idioms do not mean exactly what the words say. **I'm all ears** is an idiom. Does it really mean I'm made of all ears? No, it means **I'm listening very carefully!**

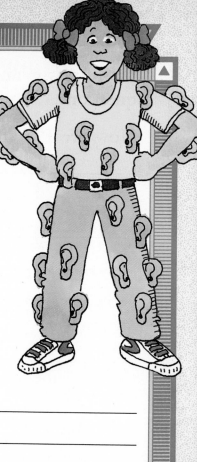

With a partner, write two idioms you know and say. Write their special meanings, too.

Idioms   Meanings

_____   _____

_____   _____

In the box below, draw a picture of one of the idioms. Draw what the words say, not what they mean.

MUFARO'S BEAUTIFUL DAUGHTERS

Cities, Deserts, Mountains, and Jungles
Yeh-Shen takes place in China, and *The Rainbow-Colored Horse* takes place in Puerto Rico. This tale takes place in Africa. Africa is a large continent made up of many kinds of people, languages, foods, music, and landscapes. With a partner, write what you know about Africa. Use the illustration on this page to get started.

Complete the story by using these words to fill in the blanks. Then write a title for the story.

temper • considerate • worthy • greed

Title: _____

There once was a village that needed a new leader. The villagers would choose one of three people. The first person was wise, but she was filled with _____. She wanted to be chief so she could keep all the best food for herself. The second person was also wise, but he had a very bad _____. Whenever things didn't go his way, he yelled and stamped his feet. The third person was perhaps not quite as wise as the others, but he was kind, _____, and always thought of other people first. So when the villagers made their choice, they chose the third person. He was the most _____ of the honor of being chief.

Reading Notes ✒ As you read *Mufaro's Beautiful Daughters,* use this space to write about the reading strategies you use. You might also write down any new words, questions, or ideas you want to remember.

_____

_____

_____

_____

_____

_____

_____

_____

_____

_____

_____

_____

_____

_____

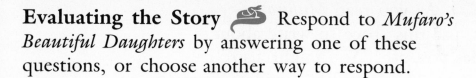
Evaluating the Story Respond to *Mufaro's Beautiful Daughters* by answering one of these questions, or choose another way to respond.

• Of the three stories you have read, which one did you like best? Why?

• Who was your favorite character? Why?

_____

_____

_____

_____

_____

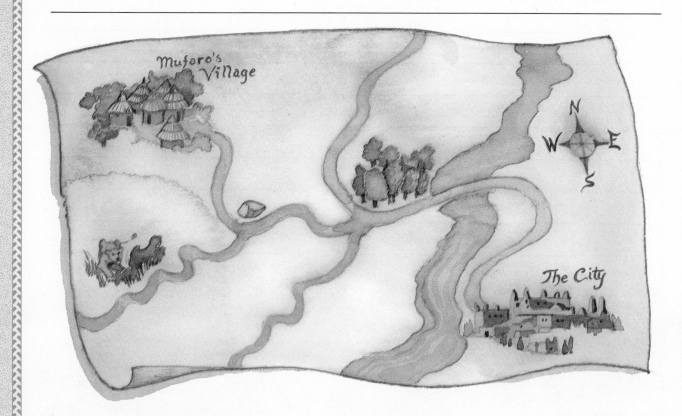

Through the Magic Forest In a small group, use this map to retell the story of *Mufaro's Beautiful Daughters*. Tell what happened to Manyara at each place, and what happened to Nyasha.

Comparing and Contrasting  In the fairy tale "Cinderella," Cinderella is kind and hard-working, while her stepsisters are mean and greedy. Cinderella is rewarded by winning the prince.

What is the theme of "Cinderella"? _____

_____

_____

_____

Think about the stories in "Once Upon a Time." Write how the theme of each story is like the theme of "Cinderella."

Yeh-Shen

_____

_____

_____

The Rainbow-Colored Horse

_____

_____

_____

Mufaro's Beautiful Daughters

_____

_____

_____

A Message to the Queen Would you know how to be a good queen? Do you think Nyasha will know what to do? With a partner, discuss how a good queen should rule her kingdom. Then write a letter to Nyasha. Give her advice about being a good queen.

Dear Nyasha,

Your humble friends,

_____

_____

A Theme PROJECT

LAND OF IMAGINATION

The Land of Imagination

Choosing and Planning

Who is your favorite fairy tale character? As a group project, create your own Land of Imagination, home to your favorite fairy tale characters.

Creating a Land of Imagination calls for a number of steps. You and your group will need to

- choose a favorite fairy tale character
- draw the character in his or her home
- make a plan for a map
- come up with a list of assignments that group members can sign up to do
- make the map
- decide where to display your map
- decide how to help visitors find their way through the Land of Imagination

Some fairy tale characters are listed below. Work with the group to add other names to the list. If you need help, look in the library.

Fiction books are stories that are made up by the author. In the library, these books are grouped together. They are arranged alphabetically by the authors' last names. If you do not know the author of a fairy tale, look up the subject *Fairy Tales* in the card catalog.

Cinderella

Hansel and Gretel

_____

_____

_____

_____

_____

_____

Look over the list, and choose a character. Then decide on the type of house for your character. Where will you place the character in the house? In a doorway or at an open window? In a garden?

Checkpoint

The character I chose is _____

Here is how I will show the character and the house: _____

_____

Now that you have chosen your character, plan with your group how to set up the map.

- Decide on the map features to include — rivers, mountains, lakes, cities, roads.
- Decide where to place the houses.
- List the materials needed to make the map — butcher paper, tempera paints, paintbrushes, felt-tip markers.
- Come up with a list of assignments. Examples: gathering materials, sketching features on the map, painting, placing houses on the map.

> A **map** is a simple drawing of an area. Only the important details are shown. The names of cities, mountains, rivers, roads, and other places and things are often included. Small pictures, or symbols, stand for the things shown on a map. A map key, or legend, explains what each symbol means.

Checkpoint

My assignment: _____

To complete my assignment, I will: _____

_____

Putting It Together

Now you are ready to make your map of the Land of Imagination. Here is a checklist to help you keep track of your progress.

- ☐ All the characters and homes are made.
- ☐ The art supplies have been collected.
- ☐ The features on the map have been drawn and painted.
- ☐ A key has been included to explain the features.
- ☐ The houses have been placed on the map.

Now that the map is complete, you and your group must decide how to help visitors find their way around your Land of Imagination. Here are suggestions for different guides. Check the idea you like best, or make up your own.

Steps for writing directions:

- Write a sentence that tells the main idea. Example: If you want to take a snooze, here's how to join the folks at Sleeping Beauty's castle.
- Write the steps in order. Use order words, such as *first*, *next*, *then*, and *finally*. Use direction words such as *left*, *right*, *north*, and *south*.
- Think about your purpose (the reason you are writing) and your audience (your readers).

☐ **Create a visitor's handbook.**

- List the houses in the order you want a traveler to visit them.
- Give directions for finding each house.
- Draw a picture of the house.
- Write a brief description of the house and the character who lives there.

Other ideas: _____

_____

☐ Create a travel pamphlet.

- Explain why visitors should come to the Land of Imagination.

- Make a list of the places to visit.

- Give suggestions for where to stay, where to eat *(The Three Bears make excellent porridge!)*, and what to avoid *(Don't buy any apples!)*.

- Include pictures in your pamphlet.

- Make a cover for the pamphlet.

Other ideas: _____

☐ Create a "Land of Imagination Census."

- List the name of each character and his or her address and telephone number.

- Tell the age and occupation of the character.

- List the names of other family members.

Other ideas: _____

PORRIDGE

An Idea of My Own: _____

_____

A Description of How I Will Do It: _____

_____

_____

Presenting the Project

Where will you display your map?

❒ in the classroom

❒ in the school library

Whom will you invite to see your map?

❒ students in other third-grade classes

❒ students in the first and second grades

❒ parents and teachers

How will you share your guide with others?

❒ Make one copy of the handbook, pamphlet, or census report, and display it next to the map.

❒ Make several copies of the guide to distribute to visitors. (Check with your teacher to see where you could have copies made.)

Other ideas for presenting your map: _____

_____

_____

_____

_____

_____

_____

_____

_____

_____

My Own Project Plan

Plan your own project. Use the ideas that come to you when you read "Once Upon a Time." Decide first if you will work alone or with others. Then use this sheet to make a plan.

Exploring Ideas

What things would you like to learn about? List as many ideas as you can think of:

_____

_____

Choose the best idea: _____

Give one reason why that topic is a good choice: _____

_____

_____

Gathering Information

Where will you find the information you want? Check the sources you will use.

❏ Encyclopedias   ❏ Nonfiction books

❏ Magazines

❏ Other _____

Presenting Your Project

How will you share what you have learned? Check the project you will do.

❏ Written report   ❏ Speech   ❏ Model

❏ Poster

❏ Other _____

Writing a Fairy Tale

Prewriting

It's storytelling time and time for you to write a fairy tale. You can write a tale set long ago or one that takes place in the present. Your tale can take place in a foreign land or in your own town or city. Lots of things can go into a fairy tale. Add your own ideas to this pot. Stir them up!

DARK FOREST

DRAGONS

MAGIC TREE

Choosing a Topic What will be in your fairy tale? Use this question to help you to decide.

• Who will read my fairy tale?

Talk to a partner about your fairy tale ideas.
Circle the idea you will use.

Exploring Your Topic   Now that you have chosen a topic, use the guide to plan your fairy tale.

1. How will your fairy tale begin? Where and when does it take place?

_____

_____

2. What problem does the main character have?

_____

_____

3. What magic creatures or objects will you include?

_____

_____

4. What events will take place?

   a. _____

   b. _____

   c. _____

   d. _____

5. How will your tale end?

_____

_____

Talk about your fairy tale with a partner. Then make changes to your plan.

SAVE ME, PRINCESS!

Drafting

Use a separate sheet of paper for your first draft. Don't worry about making mistakes. As you work, keep this question in mind.

- What are some things the characters might say to one another?

Revising

Read your fairy tale. Can you find ways to make your tale better? Now is the time to add more details.

Writing Conference Work with a group to discuss your work. Read your story aloud. Then use the questions below for your discussion.

Questions for a Conference

- Does the order of events make sense?
- Does the dialogue (the things characters say) sound real?
- Are there any parts that aren't clear?

After you discuss your fairy tale, make changes.

Proofreading

Now is the time to correct your mistakes, using the Proofreading Checklist to help you.

Proofreading Checklist

- ☐ Did I indent all paragraphs?
- ☐ Did I use capital letters for proper nouns?
- ☐ Did I spell each word correctly?

Did you use dialogue correctly in your story? Use the chart below to make sure.

Punctuation for Dialogue

- Use **quotation marks** (" ") around a person's exact words.
- Use a **comma** to set off a person's exact words.
- Begin the first word of a quotation with a capital letter and put an end mark before the last quotation mark.
  Randy asked, "How deep is the sea?"

Publishing

Copy your fairy tale neatly, and add a fairy tale title. Here are some ideas for sharing your work with others.

- Make finger puppets for a puppet show and act out your fairy tale.

- Read your fairy tale to a younger child.

Write your own ideas for sharing here.

_____

_____

_____

Writer's Log Did you have any problems writing your fairy tale? How did you solve them? Write what you have learned about writing fairy tales.

_____

_____

PUERTO RICO

Before Reading

SQRR STRATEGY

Survey what you are going to read. Read the titles and headings. Look at the pictures and captions. Read the Thinking Focus and Key Terms on page 200 and the Review questions on page 208. Write what you learned.

_____

_____

_____

_____

During Reading

Read the heading on page 201. Turn this heading into a question. Then read to find the answer to your question. Write the answer under the question.

Question: _____

_____

_____

Answer: _____

_____

_____

_____

Read the heading on page 202. Turn this heading into a question. Read to find the answer to your question. Write the answer under the question.

Question: _____

_____

Answer: _____

_____

Now do the same for the two headings on page 204. Turn each heading into a question. Write the question on the line. Read to find the answer. Then write the answer under the question. (Hint: You must read pages 204–207 before you can answer the first question.)

First Question: _____

_____

Answer: _____

_____

Second Question: _____

_____

Answer: _____

_____

Use a separate piece of paper to write a question for the heading on page 206. Then read to find the answer. Write the answer under the question. Do the same for page 207.

After Reading

Reread the selection headings and think about the questions you wrote. Review the answers to your questions.

Finding Main Ideas and Supporting Details

On the lines below, write the main idea or ideas in each section of this selection. Also write one or two details that support each main idea.

The Island of Puerto Rico
(page 201)

Main Ideas: _____

_____

_____

_____

Supporting Details:

_____

_____

_____

The People (pages 202–203)

Main Ideas: _____

_____

_____

_____

Supporting Details:

_____

_____

_____

_____

Three Different Places
(pages 204–207)

Main Ideas: _____

_____

_____

_____

Supporting Details:

_____

_____

_____

_____

Summarizing Informational Text To sum up "Puerto Rico," write the main ideas in your own words. Leave out details that are not important. Write your summary on another piece of paper.

Follow the directions below.

1. Draw a circle around the right answer.
Puerto Rico is a

a. state   **c.** commonwealth

b. country   **d.** continent

2. Write the word that completes the sentence.

The main language of Puerto Rico is

_____ .

French   English

Spanish   Puerto Rican

**3. Write _T_ if the sentence is true.
Write _F_ if it is false.**

_____ El Yunque is a large city in Puerto Rico.

4. Fill in the circle next to the right answer.

What can Puerto Ricans do?

◯ vote for the President of the United States

◯ travel to the United States without a passport

5. Write the letter of the right meaning on the line in front of the word it matches.

_____ island

_____ peninsula

a. a body of land with water on three sides

b. a body of land surrounded by water

MY READING LOG

Name of Book _____

Author _____

This book is about _____

_____

_____

_____

_____

_____

_____

_____

Name of Book _____

Author _____

This book is about _____

_____

_____

_____

_____

_____

_____

Name of Book _____

Author _____

This book is about _____

_____

_____

_____

_____

_____

Name of Book _____

Author _____

This book is about _____

_____

_____

_____

_____

_____

Name of Book _____

Author _____

This book is about _____

_____

_____

_____

_____

Name of Book _____

Author _____

This book is about _____

_____

_____

_____

_____

Name of Book _____

Author _____

This book is about _____

_____

_____

_____

_____

Name of Book _____

Author _____

This book is about _____

_____

_____

_____

_____

Name of Book _____

Author _____

This book is about _____

_____

_____

_____

_____

_____

Name of Book _____

Author _____

This book is about _____

_____

_____

_____

_____

_____

Name of Book _____

Author _____

This book is about _____

_____

_____

_____

_____

_____

Name of Book _____

Author _____

This book is about _____

_____

_____

_____

_____

_____

Name of Book _____

Author _____

This book is about _____

_____

_____

_____

_____

_____

_____

Name of Book _____

Author _____

This book is about _____

_____

_____

_____

_____

_____

Name of Book _____

Author _____

This book is about _____

_____

_____

_____

_____

_____

_____

Name of Book _____

Author _____

This book is about _____

_____

_____

_____

_____

_____

_____

Name of Book _____

Author _____

This book is about _____

_____

_____

_____

_____

_____

_____

STUDENT
JOURNAL
HANDBOOK

STUDENT JOURNAL HANDBOOK

Contents

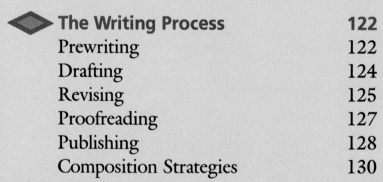

READING STRATEGIES

 ## Reading New Words

When you come to a word you cannot read:

Use Context

AND

Use Phonics

AND

Think about words that you know that are like this word. Use word parts.

Try to say the word.
Does it sound like a real word?

Check:
Does the word make sense in the sentence?
Does the word have the right sounds for the letters?

If the word doesn't make sense or you don't know its meaning — use the <u>glossary</u> or <u>dictionary</u>.

If you still can't read the word, ask for HELP.

Preview and Predict

Before Reading

Preview the selection.
- Read the title.
- Look at the pictures.
- Read a few paragraphs.

What clues do you have about the story?
What do you already know about the topic?

Predict
- What do you think is likely to happen in the story?
- What do you think you will learn?

During Reading
- Think about your predictions.
- As you get new information, change your predictions if you need to.

After Reading
- Think back to your first predictions.
- Did new information cause you to change them? In what ways?

 ## Story Map Prediction

Sometimes when you preview a story, you may want to use a
Story Map to help you think through some predictions.

Before Reading

Preview the story.
• Look through the story and the illustrations to get an
idea of what the story will be about.

Think through as much of the **Story Map** as you can.

Try to predict:
• When and where the
story takes place

• Who the main *characters* are

• What the *problem* might be

• Some things that might
happen in the story

• How the problem might be
solved

Story Map Prediction
Setting
Time
Place

Character(s)

Problem

Events

Ending

During Reading

Change or add to your **Story Map** as you get new information.

After Reading

Finish your **Story Map** by telling how the story ended, if it is different from what you predicted.

Think about how your **Story Map** changed as you read the story.

Hint:
This **Story Map** can also be used to help you **summarize** a story.

 Preview and Self-Question
Nonfiction

Before Reading

Preview the selection.
Think of the questions that might be answered by this text.

During Reading

Think about your questions as you read.

After Reading

Think back over your questions.
Which questions were answered by the text?

Stop and Think

When you do not understand what you are reading . . .

1. **Stop** and **think** about what you have read so far.

2. Look over the pages you have read.
   • Pay attention to illustrations, headings, and words in special type.

3. Think about <u>why</u> you might be having trouble.
   Did you miss some important information?
   • Reread carefully some or all of what you have read.

   Did you change your predictions based on new information?
   • Change your predictions as needed.

   Were there key words you did not know?
   • Use what you know about **Reading New Words.**

4. Read ahead. More information may help you understand better.

If you are still confused, ask someone for HELP.

 ## Summarizing Stories

Think about the story you just read.

1. **Setting**
   Where and when did the story take place?

2. **Characters**
   Who were the main characters in the story?

3. **Problem**
   What was the major problem in the story?

4. **Action**
   What were the major events in the story?

5. **Ending**
   How was the major problem solved?

6. **Theme**
   Did the author have a message?
   What was it?

If you cannot remember parts of the story . . .
- Reread some of the story.
- Talk with someone who has read the story.

Summarizing Informational Text

When you want to remember the most important ideas in the text you have read . . .

1. Look over the text.
   Identify the topic.

2. Reread and think about any parts you do not understand.

3. Find sentences that tell main ideas about the topic.

OR

Make your own main idea sentences.

4. Ask yourself:
   • Am I including the most important ideas?
   • Is my summary clear?

Hints:
• Leave out information that is not important.
• Leave out information that is repeated.
• Group together similar ideas.

 ## K-W-L

When you are reading informational texts, use a K-W-L chart to help you better understand what you read.

Before Reading

1. Identify the topic of the text.
2. Write what you already KNOW about the topic.
3. Write what you WANT to find out about the topic.

During Reading

1. Read the text, keeping in mind <u>what you want to find out</u>.
2. Sometimes you will want to use the K-W-L chart as you read:
   • Jot down information you learn and new questions you think of.

After Reading

1. Write what you have LEARNED about the topic.
2. Check your WANT list to see what questions were answered.
   • List questions you still want answered.
3. Review your KNOW list.
   • Is any of that information incorrect?
   • Is there information you would still like to know about?

K-W-L Chart

Topic :

What I KNOW	What I WANT to find out	What I LEARNED

Hint:
Sometimes you may want to fill out a K-W-L chart with a partner or a group.

 ## SQRR

Before Reading

Survey
Look over what you are going to read.
Read the titles and headings.
Look at the pictures and captions.

During Reading

Question
Turn each heading into a question.
Read
Answer each question.

After Reading

Review
Reread the headings.
See if you can answer your questions.

THE WRITING PROCESS

 Prewriting

Sometimes you are spilling over with ideas for writing. Other times your mind may feel blank. What do you do then?

First, think about your purpose. Are you going to write a report, a mystery story, or a story about yourself?

Then think about who your readers are going to be. What would they like to hear about?

Here are some ways to get your ideas flowing.

How to get ideas

- Look at magazine pictures. Write down ideas.
- List unusual things that have happened to you.
- Write down five things you wonder about.
- Look through your family's photo album.
- With a friend, list things you know how to do.
- Look around your room for reminders of fun things you've done.

Suppose you have a long list of ideas. How do you choose just one to write about? Talk about your ideas with a friend. You can also ask yourself these questions:

- Which idea would I most like to write about?
- Which do I know or remember most about?
- Which would my readers like best?

Nathan decided to write about something scary that had happened to him. He knew his friends liked scary stories. Nathan thought about different times when he had been scared. He made this list of his favorite ideas.

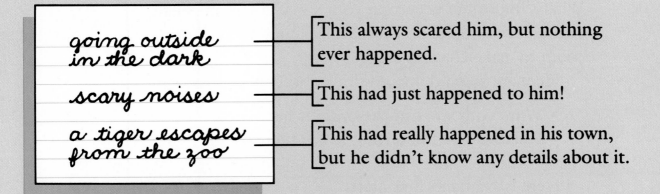

going outside in the dark — [This always scared him, but nothing ever happened.

scary noises — [This had just happened to him!

a tiger escapes from the zoo — [This had really happened in his town, but he didn't know any details about it.

Nathan talked about the ideas with his friend Kim. He decided to write about the scary noises.

Making a cluster can help you explore your story idea. Put your topic in a circle in the middle of a piece of paper. Put words or sentences that pop into your head into circles around your topic. Draw lines to show how the ideas connect.

Nathan made a cluster for his story about scary noises. Then he told his story to Kim.

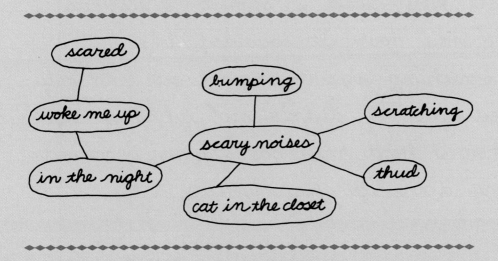

Drafting

Now comes the fun part. You can start writing! Use your cluster to help you write a first draft. Your first draft is your first try, so don't worry about mistakes. What's important is getting your story down on paper. Remember to write on every other line so you will have room to make changes later.

Here are some things to think about as you write.

- Write your story in the order it happened.
- Start with an interesting first sentence.

Here is Nathan's first draft.

The scarey noises ~~got~~ woke me
up in the middle of the night.
There were scratchings and thuds.
Boy, was I scared! I listned
at my door. It sounded like
something was trying to get into my
bedroom I didn't no what to do.
then I herd my cat cryng. i opened
my door. It was my cat.

3 ◆ Revising

Now you've got your story down on paper. That was the hardest step. You may really like what you've written, but you can probably make it clearer or more interesting. Read your story to yourself, and ask:

- Where can I use more exact words?
- Where can I add details?
- Can I make the ending more exciting?

Read your story to a partner or your group. Then talk about it with them. Do they have ideas to make your story better? You can ask the questions below to help your discussion.

Questions for a conference

- Is the beginning interesting?
- Is the story easy to follow?
- Do the actions and feelings seem real?

Nathan read his story to Kim. Kim listened closely. Then they talked about Nathan's story. Here is the conference Nathan had with Kim.

Think about what your partner said. Read your draft again. Can you make it better? Write between the lines or in the margins. Cross out or move words. Your draft will probably look very messy, but don't worry. Just make sure you can read it! You can make a neat copy and correct mistakes later.

Nathan read his draft once again. He added and changed words to make his story clearer. Here is Nathan's revised story.

Bump. Scratch. Thud. Oh no! Who was
~The scarey noises ~~got~~ woke me
trying^ to get into my room? I sat
up in the middle of the night.
straight up in bed.
~~There were scratchings and thuds.~~
                                    got out of bed and
        Boy, was I scared! ~~I~~ listned
sneeked to   The noises kept on.
~~at my door. It sounded like~~
 ^
~~something was trying to get into my~~
~~bedroom~~ I didn't no what to do.
                  a meow
then I herd ~~my~~ cat cryng. i opened
                  ^
my door. It was my cat. She had been
closed in the hall closet by mistake.
I laughed and laughed.

 4 ◆ **Proofreading**

Slowly read what you have written. Check for mistakes, word by word, and correct them.

- Use the proofreading checklist and marks.
- Use a dictionary to check spelling.

Proofreading Checklist	**Proofreading Marks**
Did I	ᚷ Indent a paragraph.
✔ 1. use complete sentences?	∧ Add something.
✔ 2. use capital letters and end marks correctly?	℘ Take out something.
✔ 3. use other punctuation marks correctly?	≡ Capitalize.
✔ 4. indent each paragraph?	/ Make a small letter.
✔ 5. spell every word correctly?	

You can still make some final changes in your story. Does it sound the way you want it to? You can ask your partner to listen to it again.

Here is part of Nathan's proofread story.

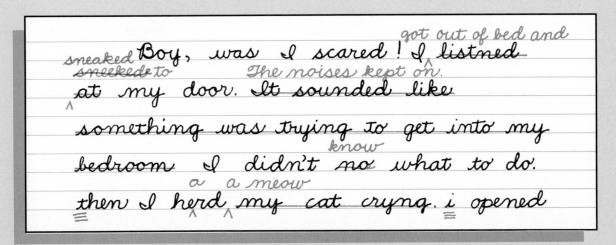

You did it! Your story is finished at last, and you're eager to share it with others. First you'll want to make a final copy.

- Copy your revised draft neatly.
- Proofread again. Correct any mistakes.
- Give your story a title.

Night Scare

Bump. Scratch. Thud. Oh no! Who was trying to get into my room? I sat straight up in bed.

Boy was I scared! I got out of bed and sneaked to my door. The noises kept on. I didn't know what to do. Then I heard a meow. I opened my door. It was my cat. She had been closed in the hall closet by mistake. I laughed and laughed.

Ideas for sharing

- Add photographs or drawings to your story. Make it into a booklet.
- Read and show your story to your friends.

Nathan rewrote his story and gave it a title. He added a photograph of his cat at the end. Then he shared the story with his friend next door.

COMPOSITION STRATEGIES

How to Write a Story

A **story** can be a mystery, an adventure, or a fairy tale. It can take place long ago, now, or in the future. The characters can be real or make-believe.

Guides for Writing a Story

1. Think about your purpose. What kind of story do you want to write? Think about your audience. Who will read your story?
2. Think about the setting. Where and when will your story happen? Think about your characters. Will one of your characters have a problem to solve?
3. Write a good beginning for your story. Tell who or what the story is about.
4. Tell what happens in the middle of your story.
5. Write an ending for your story that makes sense. The reader should feel that the story has ended.
6. Write a good title to get your reader's attention.

A Friend for Peter

The Porcupine family lived under a cabin near a beautiful lake. They were all very happy until Peter began school.

On the first day of school, Peter came home crying. His mother hugged him carefully. Then she asked him why he was so sad.

"No one wants to be friends with a porcupine!" he cried. "All the other animals run away when I go near them. I think they're afraid of me. What can I do?"

THE
WRITING
PROCESS

How to Write a Research Report

A **research report** gives facts about a certain subject. Reports are a good way to share your interests with others.

Guides for Writing a Research Report

1. Think about your purpose. What do you want your readers to learn? Think about your audience. Who will read your report?
2. Choose a topic that interests you and one that is not too broad or too narrow.
3. Write questions about your topic that you will answer in your report. Use reference books and nonfiction books about your subject to get the information to answer your questions.
4. Take notes from more than one book. Write just enough to remember the important facts.
5. When you write your report, your questions can become the topic sentences of your paragraphs. Use your notes to write supporting details.
6. Add an interesting title to your report.

The Secret of Silk

What is silk? Silk is a strong thread-like fiber that is used to make cloth.

How is silk made? First, the silkworm makes silk fiber in its body. It uses the fiber to spin a cocoon. Next, the cocoon is soaked in hot water. Then the very thin threads of silk are unwound. Several threads are put together to make a thicker thread that will be spun into cloth.

THE SPELLING GUIDE

 How to Study a Word

1 LOOK at the word.
- What does the word mean?
- What letters are in the word?
- Name and touch each letter.

2 SAY the word.
- Listen for the consonant sounds.
- Listen for the vowel sounds.

3 THINK about the word.
- How is each sound spelled?
- Close your eyes and picture the word.
- What familiar spelling patterns do you see?
- What other words have the same spelling patterns?

4 WRITE the word.
- Think about the sounds and the letters.
- Form the letters correctly.

5 CHECK the spelling.
- Did you spell the word the same way it is spelled in your word list?
- If you did not spell the word correctly, write the word again.

Words Often Misspelled

above
again
already
answer
any
are
bear
beautiful
been
believe

beyond
blue
both
bought
boxing
bread
break
breakfast
breath
brother

brought
buy
caught
ceiling
certain
chief
children
choice
color
comb
come

cough
could
country
daily
daughter
dead
death
do
does
doesn't

dollar
done
door
double
dying
early
electric
enough
eye
falling

feet
fought
friend
from
front
ghost
give
glove
gone
great
guess

half
have
head
heard
heart
heavy
helpful
I
island
judge

July
June
key
large
laugh
let's
libraries
listen
live
lose

love
lying
many
message
money
move
neighbor
noise
no one
none
nothing

o'clock
of
often
ought
pear
people
picnic
pink
pretty
rebuild

roar
rolling
rough
rule
said
school
sew
some
son
spread

straight
sure
taught
tear
teeth
their
there
they
they're
think
though

thought
through
to
toe
too
touch
traveling
trouble
two
until

unusual
voice
want
warm
was
wash
watch
weigh
what
where

who
woman
won
wonderful
won't
word
work
worried
you
young
your

The Hard-boiled Egg Fad

The Vowel Sounds in few, school, **and** put

Read Guideline 3 on page 141 to help you learn to spell these words.

Spelling Words
1. few
2. school
3. hood
4. put
5. knew
6. smooth
7. stood
8. full

Challenge Words
1. soothe
2. shampoo
3. jewel
4. crooked

Your Own Words

Add your own spelling words on the back. ⟶

135

Otis's Scientific Experiment

Words with Suffixes

Read Guideline 2 on page 141 to help you learn to spell these words.

Spelling Words
1. teacher
2. careful
3. sadly
4. loudly
5. useful
6. helper
7. player
8. hopeful

Challenge Words
1. suddenly
2. exactly
3. colorful
4. peaceful

Your Own Words

Add your own spelling words on the back. ⟶

135

Henry Writes a Letter

Words with Prefixes

Read Guideline 1 on page 141 to help you learn to spell these words.

Spelling Words
1. reread
2. unlike
3. remake
4. retell
5. unsafe
6. rewrite
7. unlock
8. unable

Challenge Words
1. unsure
2. unusual
3. review
4. unimportant

Your Own Words

Add your own spelling words on the back. ⟶

135

SPELLING AND WRITING WORD LISTS

Your Own Words

1. _____
2. _____
3. _____
4. _____
5. _____
6. _____
7. _____
8. _____

Writer's Words from the Story

You may want to use these words in your own writing.

1. problem
2. difficult
3. bother
4. ignore

How to Study a Word

LOOK at the word.
SAY the word.
THINK about the word.
WRITE the word.
CHECK the spelling.

SPELLING AND WRITING WORD LISTS

Your Own Words

1. _____
2. _____
3. _____
4. _____
5. _____
6. _____
7. _____
8. _____

Writer's Words from the Story

You may want to use these words in your own writing.

1. experiment
2. idea
3. prove
4. lesson

How to Study a Word

LOOK at the word.
SAY the word.
THINK about the word.
WRITE the word.
CHECK the spelling.

SPELLING AND WRITING WORD LISTS

Your Own Words

1. _____
2. _____
3. _____
4. _____
5. _____
6. _____
7. _____
8. _____

Writer's Words from the Story

You may want to use these words in your own writing.

1. fad
2. popular
3. giggles
4. tease

How to Study a Word

LOOK at the word.
SAY the word.
THINK about the word.
WRITE the word.
CHECK the spelling.

The Loch Ness Monster

Spelling the First Sound in city

Read Guideline 6 on page 142 to help you learn to spell these words.

Spelling Words
1. once
2. race
3. city
4. ice
5. place
6. circle
7. since
8. circus

Challenge Words
1. certain
2. excited
3. distance
4. century

Your Own Words

Add your own spelling words on the back. ⟶

137

The Long-Lost Coelacanth

The Vowel + r Sounds in first

Read Guideline 5 on page 142 to help you learn to spell these words.

Spelling Words
1. first
2. were
3. turn
4. world
5. her
6. girl
7. work
8. hurt

Challenge Words
1. preserve
2. perfect
3. thorough
4. purpose

Your Own Words

Add your own spelling words on the back. ⟶

137

The Titanic: Lost and Found

Vowel + r Sounds

Read Guideline 4 on page 141 to help you learn to spell these words.

Spelling Words
1. near
2. north
3. start
4. apart
5. hear
6. shore
7. year
8. alarm

Challenge Words
1. compartment
2. explore
3. fortune
4. argue

Your Own Words

Add your own spelling words on the back. ⟶

137

SPELLING AND WRITING WORD LISTS

Your Own Words

1. _____
2. _____
3. _____
4. _____
5. _____
6. _____
7. _____
8. _____

Writer's Words from the Story

You may want to use these words in your own writing.

1. ocean
2. voyage
3. passenger
4. captain

How to Study a Word

LOOK at the word.
SAY the word.
THINK about the word.
WRITE the word.
CHECK the spelling.

SPELLING AND WRITING WORD LISTS

Your Own Words

1. _____
2. _____
3. _____
4. _____
5. _____
6. _____
7. _____
8. _____

Writer's Words from the Story

You may want to use these words in your own writing.

1. strange
2. creature
3. search
4. discover

How to Study a Word

LOOK at the word.
SAY the word.
THINK about the word.
WRITE the word.
CHECK the spelling.

SPELLING AND WRITING WORD LISTS

Your Own Words

1. _____
2. _____
3. _____
4. _____
5. _____
6. _____
7. _____
8. _____

Writer's Words from the Story

You may want to use these words in your own writing.

1. monster
2. dragon
3. haunt
4. spooky

How to Study a Word

LOOK at the word.
SAY the word.
THINK about the word.
WRITE the word.
CHECK the spelling.

Mufaro's Beautiful Daughters

Homophones

Read Guideline 9 on page 142 to help you learn to spell these words.

Spelling Words

1. two
2. to
3. too
4. no
5. know
6. there
7. their
8. they're

Challenge Words

1. through
2. threw
3. heard
4. herd

Your Own Words

Add your own spelling words on the back. ⟶

139

The Rainbow-Colored Horse

Contractions

Read Guideline 8 on page 142 to help you learn to spell these words.

Spelling Words

1. isn't
2. don't
3. you'll
4. hadn't
5. I'm
6. we're
7. they've
8. it's

Challenge Words

1. doesn't
2. who's
3. shouldn't
4. let's

Your Own Words

Add your own spelling words on the back. ⟶

139

Yeh-Shen

Spelling the First Sound in join

Read Guideline 7 on page 142 to help you learn to spell these words.

Spelling Words

1. join
2. jacket
3. age
4. large
5. page
6. jar
7. stage
8. orange

Challenge Words

1. gentle
2. village
3. jealous
4. manage

Your Own Words

Add your own spelling words on the back. ⟶

139

SPELLING AND WRITING WORD LISTS

Your Own Words

1. _____
2. _____
3. _____
4. _____
5. _____
6. _____
7. _____
8. _____

Writer's Words from the Story

You may want to use these words in your own writing.

1. beautiful
2. orphan
3. angry
4. comfort

How to Study a Word

LOOK at the word.
SAY the word.
THINK about the word.
WRITE the word.
CHECK the spelling.

140

SPELLING AND WRITING WORD LISTS

Your Own Words

1. _____
2. _____
3. _____
4. _____
5. _____
6. _____
7. _____
8. _____

Writer's Words from the Story

You may want to use these words in your own writing.

1. stable
2. saddle
3. reins
4. swift

How to Study a Word

LOOK at the word.
SAY the word.
THINK about the word.
WRITE the word.
CHECK the spelling.

140

SPELLING AND WRITING WORD LISTS

Your Own Words

1. _____
2. _____
3. _____
4. _____
5. _____
6. _____
7. _____
8. _____

Writer's Words from the Story

You may want to use these words in your own writing.

1. journey
2. travel
3. toward
4. arrive

How to Study a Word

LOOK at the word.
SAY the word.
THINK about the word.
WRITE the word.
CHECK the spelling.

140

Spelling Guidelines

1

A **prefix** is a word part added to the beginning of a base word. It adds meaning to the base word. These word parts are prefixes: **re-** and **un-**.

rejoin   **re**use
unfair   **un**wrap

2

A **suffix** is a word part added to the end of a base word. It adds meaning to the base word. These word parts are suffixes: **-ful**, **-ly**, and **-er**.

thank**ful**   use**ful**
slow**ly**   farm**er**

3

The long **u** sound in **spoon** may be spelled with the pattern **oo**. The long **u** sound in **chew** may be spelled with the pattern **ew**.

t**oo**th   r**oo**t
dr**ew**   fl**ew**

The vowel sound in **cook** may be spelled with the pattern **oo** or **u**.

sh**oo**k   w**oo**d
p**u**sh   p**u**ll

4

The vowel + **r** sounds in **harm** can be spelled with the pattern **ar**.

sm**ar**t   M**ar**ch
d**ar**k   **ar**t

The vowel + **r** sounds in **hear** can be spelled with the pattern **ear**.

ear   f**ear**
y**ear**   cl**ear**

The vowel + **r** sounds in **corn** can be spelled with the pattern **or** or **ore**.

st**or**m   f**or**ty
ch**ore**   st**ore**

5 ◇

The vowel + **r** sounds in **dirt** can be spelled with the pattern **er, ir, ur,** or **or.**

serve	bird
nurse	word

6 ◇

The **s** sound in **pencil** can be spelled with the consonant **c** when **c** is followed by **i** or **e.**

city	circus
nice	dance

7 ◇

The **j** sound in **just** can be spelled with the consonant **j** or with the consonant **g** followed by **e.**

jump	jeans
cage	orange

8 ◇

A **contraction** is a short way of saying or writing two or more words. An apostrophe takes the place of one or more letters.

aren't	couldn't
wasn't	he's
you're	I'd

9 ◇

Homophones are words that sound the same but have different spellings and meanings.

knew	new
our	hour